# Second Helping

by

# Egton Bridge Writers' Group

First published in October 2011
by
Fryup Press, Bracken Hill, Glaisdale
Whitby, N.Yorkshire, YO21 2QZ
www.annbowes.co.uk


ISBN Number  978-0-9545951-9-7

Other published work by
Egton Bridge Writers' Group

*Bilberry Pie*
*and other tasty tales*

Printed in Great Britain
by
York Publishing Services
York

# Egton Bridge Writers' Group

Egton Bridge Writers' Group, formed in 2001, meets on a monthly basis in the quiet village of Egton Bridge in the Esk Valley.

'Second Helping', the Group's latest anthology, is a selection of writing inspired and developed through the activities and collaborative work of the group.

## Contributing Members

Ainsley

Pat Almond

Ann Bowes
    Published work: *Riding for Life* and *Friends Forever*

Alan Brighouse

Jenny Burgoyne

Pat Henderson

Harry Nicholson
    Published work: *Tom Fleck*

Julia Organ

Kate Trewren

Hilary Walker

Paul Wedgwood
    Published work: *A Moorland Tale*


Co-editors: Ann Bowes and Jenny Burgoyne

Typeset and format: Ann Bowes

Cover design and photo: Ann Bowes

# Bilberry Pie
## and other tasty tales

The group's first anthology was published in 2006 by Fryup Press, a newly established publisher based in the Esk Valley.

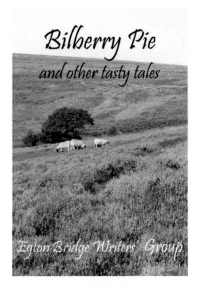

In 2007 'Bilberry Pie' won a national literary competition organized by the David St John Thomas Charitable Trust in conjunction with Writers' News and Writing Magazine. It came first in the 'Anthology of the Year' class. Members of the group were invited to the prize-giving held at the Majestic Hotel in Harrogate to receive a cup and cheque for £100.

Over 500 copies of this book have been sold, enabling the group to fund the publication of 'Second Helping' which they hope will be equally successful.

Members of the group, with Richard West (trustee) and David St. John Thomas (founder of the Trust), proudly displaying their certificate, cup and cheque at Harrogate.

*Photo: A Bowes*

4

# Contents

*Photo: A Bowes*

*"Elsewhere you have to go in search of the beautiful views; here they come and offer themselves to be looked at."*

A traveller's response to the North York Moors in conversation with Canon Atkinson of Danby.

('Forty Years in a Moorland Parish', 1891)

*Photo: A Bowes*

*"Sometimes I see old Esk in fury roll*
*Or fish, or walk, or swim the silent pool."*

John Castillo of Lealholm, the 'Bard of the Dales', 1792-1845

# Forgotten Fare

## Fairies of Fryup Plain

The moonlight woke Billy and he knelt on his bed looking outside, thinking about his granddad's story. Should he go? It was now or never. He'd do it. He scrambled off his bed and quickly pulled on his clothes. He opened the bedroom door and peeped out. All was in darkness. As quietly as he could he crept down the stairs and pulled on his boots and jacket. After unlocking the door he ventured out into the night.

The full moon was shining brightly, making it easy for Billy to find his way from field to field, keeping close to the stone walls, before finally climbing between the railings into the wood. It wasn't so easy walking here among the heather and dead bracken, the briars and dead branches that were strewn between the trees. Suddenly he tripped, his hands instinctively reaching out to the ground as he fell. He felt something harsh beneath his hand and, thinking it to be a short stick, picked it up. Holding it against the moonlight he realized it was a pine cone, not just a little one, but the largest he had ever seen. A huge grin spread across his little face as he shoved it into his pocket. He would have to show Granddad that one.

Peering ahead he could just see the stony outcrop from where he hoped to wait and watch. He scrambled his way towards it just as the moon went behind some clouds. Billy crouched down in the heather behind a big rock, trying to find a little shelter from the cold night wind, and waited.

The minutes ticked slowly by. Billy was beginning to think that this was not such a good idea after all. He wished he'd remembered his cap, for his ears were stinging in the frosty night air, and his toes were turning numb. He pulled the collar of his jacket up around his neck and thrust his hands deep into his pockets. The tall pine trees creaked and groaned as their lofty branches high above him swayed in the wind. He shivered, wishing the moon would come out again from behind the clouds. Surely, it must be almost midnight by now. If it

7

didn't come out soon it would be too late.  He waited another five minutes although it seemed more like thirty.

As he huddled down in the heather he could smell damp pine needles, fallen leaves and rotting twigs.  He jumped, startled by the harsh call of a nightjar as it left the cover of the trees.  He couldn't see it in the darkness but he heard its wings in flight as it passed close to him.  It had probably been disturbed by the presence of a red fox awaking from its sleep to set off on his nightly forage for food.

His granddad had told him all about the wild animals that lived around them in the countryside.  He had taught Billy many things about where the animals lived and what they ate.  Once, on one of their walks, he had shown Billy where the badgers lived, pointing out the tracks they had made as they went to and fro from the sett, their underground home.  They had found the heaps of discarded bedding, trundled out by the badgers when they had cleaned their nests.  Granddad often came to stay with them and, as well as going for walks with him, Billy loved to listen to his stories.  The story he had told earlier that evening had fascinated Billy and he hadn't been able to sleep because of thinking about it but now he was beginning to think that it had only been a story.  He had felt sure that it was a true story because the full moon had reminded Granddad about his own adventure.  Granddad often related tales to Billy about his own childhood.

Billy was beginning to wish that he had never asked about the Fairy Rings.  Somewhere in the distance an owl hooted, probably alarmed by the same red fox, still hunting through the undergrowth.  Billy was getting colder and beginning to wish he was tucked up in his warm little bed, when suddenly the moon broke from behind the clouds, its silvery light casting shadows all around.  Hardly daring to move, he watched the field opposite through the trees.  He could see nothing and just as quickly the moon disappeared behind another cloud.  Billy sighed and decided he'd had enough.  The next time the moon came out he was going home.

The clouds raced across the sky and Billy was about to stand up when his mouth opened wide in astonishment.  He stared across the open field, amazed at what he saw.  So it was true, for there, dancing round in a circle, appearing as if from nowhere, making a perfect ring, were twelve fairies.  They sparkled and shone as the silvery moonlight glistened on their translucent wings. Billy gazed in awe, hardly daring to breathe, never mind move.  Fascinated, he watched as the tiny creatures performed their ritualistic dance. Suddenly, to his dismay, he was once more clothed in darkness as more clouds blotted out the moonlight. He stood up and stretched his cramped legs, trying to get the feeling back in his numbed feet. Once more the moon appeared briefly and he stared across the field but there was nothing, nothing at all.

He waited only a moment before setting off back home. He let himself in and turned the key, waiting for the usual click. The house was silent as he pulled off his boots and hung up his jacket. He tiptoed up the stairs, crept into his room and was soon snuggled up in bed.

When Billy awoke the next morning he wondered if it had all been a dream. He dared not tell anyone; for one thing, no one would believe him but also he knew that, if he did, it would bring him bad luck, as Granddad had found to his cost. Billy sighed. Never mind, it had been an exciting dream. He was still thinking about it later as he pulled on his cap and zipped up his coat ready for school. He turned and waved to his mother as he walked down the lane to catch the bus before thrusting his hands in his pockets. There, to his amazement, he felt the giant cone.

*Ann Bowes*

Fryup Plain              *(photo - A Bowes)*

# The Old Stone Cross

There's an old stone cross; it stands there still,
Amidst the moor, up on a hill.
It's seen the centuries come and go:
Who placed it there? Who can know?

For countless years, all seasons round,
The cross erect has stood its ground.
Neath summer suns and winter blasts,
A waymark for lone travellers past,
A sign of hope for those who'd crossed
The barren moor but strayed and lost
Their way, when thickest roak
Had wrapped them in a giant's cloak.

Dour pannier-man with laden horse
Has, by the cross, steered safe his course.
Poor blessed nuns on pilgrimage
From dale to dale their trod would gauge.

Mute witness to millennia gone,
An archaic symbol, sign of One
Born long ago in far off land,
A Baby dressed by Virgin's hand
In swaddling clothes and laid in stall –
Our world would soon be in His thrall.
This pristine Child would save mankind:
Our calendar, mark off His time.

Yet still in silent vigil stands
This relic bold with outstretched hands,
Statue-still, as cold as death:
Tired ramblers pass with hoary breath.

But, what's for the cross amidst the moor?
Its end will come in time for sure,
For hardest stone returns to dust,
As each of us in sequence must.
Who can survive? What can endure?
Mortals all, we are for sure.
There is but one thing that will last;
It is His love – eternally cast.

*Ainsley*

Old Ralph Cross     *(photo - Ainsley)*

# I Know a Secret...

I know a secret. It has been my secret for twelve years now.

Along the lane from where I live hides the most peaceful and beautiful place on earth. Well... I think so, anyway.

But don't tell anyone, otherwise everyone will want to visit. It has been mine, and mine alone, for all that time. Or that is how it has always felt, ever since we moved into our present home, and I discovered it, smelling of long grass and old, damp, dripping trees.

Whenever I feel in need of a bit of tranquillity and solitude, I wander down there with my dog, Freddie. We head for the same large memorial tablet and just sit. Sometimes we sit for quite a long time. We don't move. It is a thinking stone. Well, Fred does get a bit bored and wanders off sometimes, but he doesn't go far and keeps coming back to make sure I am still where he left me. I have no idea who is buried under 'my' stone. The stone is weathered and unreadable. I like to think that it is a nice, kind person, a patient listener, who is good at keeping secrets, because I have just about discussed everything that has happened to me over the years with this person.

Where is the scene of all this serenity and therapy? It is a beautiful, little church, just outside the village of Egton, called the Mortuary Chapel, as it was built for burial purposes. It occupies the site of the original church which was pulled down and moved to its present position in 1878. The graveyard is still used to this day.

There has been a church on this site since 1349, so it seems incredible to us today that such an important and reputedly beautiful piece of our heritage would be so easily destroyed, but, like a small and perfectly formed phoenix, the little chapel has risen contentedly in its place. A comment from the parish magazine of 1945 helps shed a bit of light on it. "Few of the present generation would, of their own choice, undertake the long walk; week in, week out, exposed to all the rains that rain and the winds that blow, to worship in a cold draughty, windswept church, even though it had fine Norman pillars and arches that preached an impressive sermon all on their own." So wrote a certain Percy Burnett. And so the church was moved to a more central location in Egton and my own private little church was built in its stead. Lucky me!

When my family and I came to the village in 1996, the Mortuary Chapel had deteriorated and was in need of repair to make it safe and to protect the fabric of the building. But the air of neglect made it somehow even more precious and mysterious, and I loved it on sight. When there was a suggestion that the place be demolished there were objections, understandably, and a series of fundraising activities got the ball rolling towards saving our little chapel.

Fund raising began in 2002. My own contribution towards rescuing the chapel was to set up a fun run, along with two other people from the village, Peter Godbold and Roger Everitt, and it was an annual event here in Egton for nine years. There were raffles and tea dances, and it was heartening to be part of a village which pulled together to save something that was so precious to all of us.

Work began a short time later when John Taylor from Saltburn came to help. The stone ridge tiles and roof tiles were replaced, the pointing of the stone and refurbishing of the bell and bell tower were completed. The interior of the chapel was renovated, and James Godbold, blacksmith of this parish, made us some beautiful candle sconces. The Mortuary Chapel was beginning to look extremely smart and cared for.

And then there began to be services held there again. The pet services are amazing! Every one arrives with their pets. A mind-boggling selection of animals arrive, dragging their owners behind them. We have had a Shetland pony standing at the back, just inside the door. There was the golden retriever, looking extremely handsome in his red bandana, who insisted on howling along to every hymn. There have been cats, goldfish and guinea pigs, all lining up for their blessing. And not a cross word between them! Well... maybe a little cross word and a tiny bit of tension. But, that's churches the world over!

Work continues in the shape of rebuilding dry stone walls, and working parties have been formed to tidy the grounds and cut back trees and bushes. There is still regular maintenance to be carried out, so we were thrilled to hear that we had been awarded the conservation award for 2009 by NYMNP and NYMA. The money has been put to good use. A handsome new sign now stands proudly at the gateway explaining a little bit about the Egton Chapel. A complete history of the church is currently underway which will eventually be published, and the large, imposing door needs repairs and renovation.

So, you see, you now know my secret. And I don't really mind sharing it with you. As long as you promise to come and go quietly, and soak up the solitude and the utter peace of the place whilst you are there.

Just don't sit on my private stone, that's all. That belongs to me and Fred!

*Hilary Walker*

*Photo: H Walker*

# The Teaspoon

It was just an ordinary, silver teaspoon, quite valuable probably, being silver not plate, used to administer medicine to a very sick spinster during the flu epidemic of 1918.

May was ill, very ill. Influenza had taken her father and now seemed likely to take her. Not if she had anything to do with it, it wouldn't! She had the house now and everything to live for. 'Joseph' – his very name made her feel better. Soon he'd come clumping down the stairs from the room he rented to check on how she was feeling. He had a responsible job at the factory and had been boarding at 9, Hope Road for over a year – such a lovely, lovely man.

As if summoned by telepathy Joseph entered the room. He was carrying her medicine and a teaspoon.

"Here, have some more medicine, it will really, really help."
Carefully spooning the liquid into May's mouth, looking into her trusting eyes, Joseph felt no guilt – it would be over soon. He patted her shoulder...

"Better?"

"Oh, Joseph," she sighed.

"Oh, May," he responded with an echoing sigh: clever, duplicitous man.

Six weeks later, after the funeral, Joseph reflected upon how much the medicine had helped. Two hundred and fifty pounds worth of help, just for being a considerate lodger and nursing his landlady through – or rather, not through - the dreadful flu.

He'd prevaricated about the poison choice for a while. Scheele's Prussic Acid was the fastest acting, but arsenic was less suspicious and more readily found. She'd had some in the basement, silly woman. Yes, it had been worth the wait. Gastric upsets were all too common with the flu, especially this virulent one of the moment. He'd smashed the medicine bottle and put the shards in the dustbin. The cleaned spoon had been shoved to the back of the dresser drawer in the kitchen. May had left him the house; she'd thought the world of him, had wanted the world from him but he wasn't prepared to give it, so he'd sent her to heaven instead. Joseph kindly left the new owner the teaspoon. It was a gift, unknown and unappreciated, passed on by subsequent owners throughout the century. Then, come the millennium, it was discovered.

It was just an old, tarnished, silver teaspoon, found at the back of a kitchen drawer when Mel and Peter moved into 9 Hope Road, their first step on the property ladder. They planned to revamp the entire property, so the spoon went to the nearest charity shop together with lots of other accumulated junk. The spoon, genuine silver made in Sheffield in 1911, was snapped up by a dealer for a pound. He had a ready market for silver spoons; a jewellery maker in Tunbridge Wells always needed them for his thriving business.

Sarah is a young (well, relatively so) woman of the twenty-first century. She has a long-term partner, not a husband, and two large dogs. She wears a ring on her right index finger and often smiles down at it – the ring was a present to herself. It consists of a broad, flat, silver band with a tapering silver bar coiled around it. It's unique, ordered from the website of a firm in Tunbridge Wells and made from a silver teaspoon of vintage 1911. She knows this because there was a print-out of this information with her ring in its purple, velvet box. Other information about the history of the spoon was not provided. But the past does not have to impinge on the present. The ring is beautiful, it's shiny and modern – it lifts her spirits. The ring's history is irrelevant. Hartley said, "The past is foreign country." It is, and only invades our present if we allow it to do so.

Post Script: Joseph Johnson, erstwhile of 9 Hope Road, died of influenza in December 1918.


Note: "The past is a foreign country: they do things differently there."
L.P. Hartley.
    Prologue to "The Go Between"

*Kate Trewren*

# Out of the Darkness

It's more than just dark; it is clinging damp dark. Natural light cannot permeate this far below ground; that luxury was left behind on the surface some 500 feet above.

Walter Davies trudged the half mile through tunnels hewn out of the rock and shale below the green and fertile valleys of North Yorkshire. He earned his money in the dark and dangerous world of the mines; a world that stretches just four feet in any direction, constrained by the flickering light of candle; a world thick with the smells of sulphur, creosote from the treated timbers that supported the roof and periodically cordite and blasting powder.

Water seeped from the roof, water tainted with sulphur. Walter's boots were already wet with that water, wet that would rot the leather and devour his socks in a matter of weeks. He trudged this route six times a week, his working day stretching from 6am to 2pm.

Heading towards him through the candle-lit gloom came a figure. Walter paused to ask the Deputy about the conditions ahead. "Could be worse," said the Deputy with a smile on his lips, "but keep an ear open; it sounds to me like your section is nearing running water. The wall to the east end rings like a bell. Teck it easy Walt, I don't want to be telling that new Missus of yours that you've been washed away." Walter and the Deputy laughed as they parted, their laughter echoing from wall to wall.

Soon Walter was on his own once again. As he neared the working face he listened, trying to detect the water flow that the deputy had spoken of, but, strangely enough, the only sound he could hear was the rhythmic breathing of a person.

"And where have you been this morning?" came a voice from the darkness. "Missed the first cage did ye?" continued the voice, tinged with a strong Cornish accent.

"And good morning to you too, Mister Tremain, and why, pray tell, are you sat in the dark? Too many of the Tavern's Best Bitter left you with little or no money for the candles again?"

"You may be right," the voice retorted, "But don't tell the Missus, she'll blow her top. I've spent the rent money too! Oh, and can I owe you the powder money until payday?"

"I think," said Walter, "you still owe me from last payday!" Like so many miners Billy Tremain had no sense when it came to money.

If he had money in his pocket he would spend it; miners worked hard, drank hard and, when necessary, fought hard and because of this mentality Billy's wife and children would go hungry again this week.

Walter furnished Billy with a new candle and after much sweat and toil the first charges of the day were set. Between them several holes had been hand-drilled into the ironstone face and a charge inserted into each of the openings, covered by a plug of clay. Once the fuses had been lit, Walter and Billy made a quick exit to safety further along the tunnel. With a rush of hot air and a deafening crash the face was reduced to rubble. Billy then pushed the first of several metal tubs along the trackway towards the mound of shattered rock and within minutes of the blast, with the air still thick with dust, the two friends began the arduous task of filling the iron carts with the precious ore-rich rock. They worked hard; their wages were dependent on the amount of ore sent to the surface.

After they had filled four tubs, they heard the sound of hooves coming down the expanse of tunnels. The animal, a Dales Pony, was accompanied by a rangy youth of no more than fourteen years of age and already he had the stoop of an old man. In his free hand he carried a small metal box in which burned a candle; this illuminated his way through the labyrinth of tunnels that made up the mine. Soon, the first two metal tubs, complete with their face numbers, were hitched to the pony's harness. In a couple of minutes the lad, pony and the tubs were once more lost to the darkness.

Billy doused all but one candle as they sat to eat their food. In the murk Walter sensed they were not alone; a warm friendly feeling came over him and with it a voice and a strange sense of urgency, imminent danger. Grabbing his cache of candles and powder, Walter screamed at Billy to get up and flee. Billy, without a word, took to his heels and ran for all he was worth along the tunnel, followed closely by Walter. The tunnel rose sharply ahead. As they reached the top of the rise a wave of water caught up with the fleeing pair and soon they were waist-deep. Their candle had been extinguished and they had to move by feeling their way along the walls.

After what seemed like an eternity, Billy and Walter reached a gallery, the remains of a worked-out seam where they hauled their bedraggled bodies out of the maelstrom and onto dry ground. Walter lit a candle and they peered down into the inky black depths of swirling water below them.

From the gallery it was only a short walk to the base of the lift shaft and safety. Once there they sat in silence, reflecting on the recent happenings.

Billy was the first to recover; turning to Walter he said, "How did you know?"

Walter smiled at his companion, "I thought I heard a voice call".

*Paul Wedgwood*

*Illustration: H Walker*

# Crossing Ainthorpe Rigg

Which path to take when there are three?
All ancient, foot and hoof-trodden, loads drawn,
Across the high moorland Norse-named Rigg
To trade, to worship or to mourn.

Take Old Wife's Stones Road to Crossley Side.
Midway a smooth-faced standing stone looks west,
Set tall to guard charcoal and bone,
While, all around, cairns mark where men cleared ground,
Grew and grazed and took their rest.

Or go the Old Hell Way from Fryup Dale,
The corpse road to grey-stone Danby Church,
And hear the rattle of trundling coffin carts
Battle and lurch through drift and gale.

Or follow the Jack Sledge Road,
That carried iron and peat, lime and coal,
To the moor's rock-strewn edge,
Where hangs in air the Dancing Stone.
Who dares tread its bare stage-floor?

Whichever way it has to be
To cross the Rigg, climb in haste
And hear in the thud of the heart's beat
Ancestral feet, keeping pace.

*Jenny Burgoyne*

*Photo:*
*A Bowes*

# The Cowshed Wall

"I've still got it, Bill."

"Got what?" I take in the groove across Tom's forehead - ploughed there by years of cap wearing.

"That little skull. It's still in the sack in me rabbit shed. All this time it's been there and I've never looked at it - can't. Someone will find it when I'm gone, and then what?"

I grunt and glance at my empty glass. "Then, soon as we're done here we'll take it onto moor and bury it. That'll be a job done."

"So, we'd better have another. Same again?"

"Aye," I hand him two bob. "I'll pay."

I light my pipe and take my mind back. It was about when the first motor car came up the dale. Funny how our younger years seemed easier to get at as time passes; it's last week that foxes me. Lumley's Farm is no bother, it's as clear as a picture.

It must be thirty years ago, yet I still see those empty eye sockets: black with mould; the teeth all there except for two which the little lass must have left out for the tooth fairy. The tuft of hair still stuck to it is copper coloured, just like Missus Lumley's curls before she went white. I see myself clear as day - a young man with hard muscle and flat stomach.

Tom puts two pints on the table - they have good heads.

We were pulling down a cowshed wall - so as to take out a bulge and straighten it up. The roof sagged under the weight of crumbling sandstone slates. It was dangerous, so we took off the slates and stacked them 'heads down' in the yard. We worked in the first daylight the insides of that byre had seen for a hundred years.

I'd been clearing up the rubble around Tom's boots as my pal levered away with the wrecking-bar. 'Farmer built' it was, a 'squint-of-eye, crook-of-gob and, it'll-be-reet', sort of a wall. Stuff fell out of the rubble-fill as Tom loosened one course after another; rat bones, spuggy nests, clay pipes, a pot egg for setting under a broody, and a blackened silver fork with two prongs.

'I'm keeping an eye on you, mind,' I'd called out. 'When you get to the bag o' sovereigns I want my share.' Then - before Tom could answer - the skull fell out and he'd jumped back as it tumbled between his legs.

'This was different,' we'd agreed; so the two of us sat down on the rubble and lit our pipes while we mulled over what to do. Tom wasn't too bothered; he'd seen plenty of loose heads in the Sudan when he was with Kitchener.

The skull seemed to stare at us from where it had come to rest among the bits of lime mortar and lumps of sandstone. Tom stayed quiet for a bit, then whispered, "Do you think it's anyone we know?"

"Well, for a start, I'd say this byre's at least two hundred year auld. Could be anybody." We'd looked at each other for a while; then coughed to get the dust off our chests, took out scraps of cloth and blew our noses hard.

The woman of the house came out before we'd finished our pipes. A nice woman she was; but gossip said she'd had her troubles, she'd lost a little girl once: just vanished one day and never turned up again. But that was years before.

When we saw her coming, Tom tossed his jacket over the skull. Missus Lumley picked her way through the rubble and put down a tray of tea and scones on a flat stone. She settled her lumpy body onto a stool to have a bit of a natter while we had our break. I remember shifting a bit - the woman's foot was right next to the coat.

Missus Lumley passed round the scones and mugs of tea.

"How's your mam keeping, Bill? Are her legs any better?"

I tapped out my pipe. "No, Missus, they're not; it's the rheumatics."

Just then Francis walked past the gap in the wall, he was carrying a bucket of swill in each hand. Missus Lumley called out, "Brother, your tea's in here."

"I won't be a minute, Betty. I'll just look at the sow - to see if she's ready."

We watched Francis stop by the sow's paddock and call her. She trotted over and came alongside the fence. The sun sparkled on her ginger coat as she turned on her long legs. I could tell Francis was fond of the sow by the way he picked up a yard brush and gave her back a scratch.

"She loves this," Francis called out. "Likes her itches seeing to - her eyes are shut wi' the pleasure of it."

I thought: even though folk say he's a hard one, the man's got tender innards. We watched Francis lean over and press his hand down onto the sow's back. If her back stayed stiff and didn't sag it meant she was ready for the boar.

"Will you have another scone, Bill?" Mrs Lumley asked.

"Thanks, missus. They're just right." Chewing the scone I watched Francis carefully open the gate to the boar's pen. The beast gave a loud squeal and Francis cursed and tried to shut the gate as the boar forced its great red head through the gap.

Francis yelled out over the noise of splintering wood. The Tamworth had knocked him off his feet then rived at him with its mucky yellow tusks. Mrs Lumley set off running, but her foot got caught in the coat and pulled it away behind her. The skull rolled over so that its little eye sockets stared up and out of the cowshed and into the sky. But the woman hadn't noticed. She ran - pinny flying - across the yard shouting, "Francis! Francis!"

I ran after her, carrying the wrecking bar. Behind me, Tom scooped up the skull, shoved it into a sack, then followed us with a shovel...

That poor soul. I stare at the beer - the head's going down. She'd nursed her brother and his wound for a fortnight while the pig poison went through him. It set fire to his veins before he died.

I considered Francis again. A dark bachelor man. Kept to himself. Used to wander about, muttering. Wouldn't look you in the eye. Folk kept out of his way.

Missus Lumley was the only woman at the funeral. But the farmers had turned out in strength - they had respect for the man's ploughing. I can still see the rows of them; in black, hair combed flat, sitting upright in the pews...

The sound of dottle being scraped out of a pipe breaks my thoughts.

"Have you nodded off, Bill? That beer's gone flat."

"Sorry, Tom, I was far away - thinking of Francis Lumley; he was an odd one."

"Aye - but he was worth listening to if you got him talking. He was fed up with living in that auld house. Told me the sun had to burn on it for three month afore the damp cleared. His best coat was mouldy and smelt bad - he reckoned no lass would come near him like he was. It was getting him down; every night that same lumpy auld bed, on his own, freezing cold. He had a brother who ran away to sea to get shot of the father's hard driving. Francis reckoned his brother to be on some tropical island with dancing girls and wearing good boots and a fine hat." Tom laughs out loud and half-chokes himself with beer.

I wait for him to get his breath back. "Did Missus Lumley ever have a husband?"

23

"She never did. So there was just the two of them - brother and sister, unwedded, getting auld together. Sad really. Folk didn't ask about the husband she never had; she was just Missus Lumley - a woman who'd lost a little lass."

"And the father of the lass? I heard Francis knew who he was." I keep my voice down.

"Yes, he reckoned it was some waster who walked the 'Entire' round the farms. I remember that hoss: he was a big black Clydesdale, the sort with a deep chest and massive quarters. He'd hooves that would smother a dinner plate. He were fed like a fighting-cock, and never ridden so as to keep all his strength for covering the mares. They say the walker of the Entire was just as randy as the beast itself. By all accounts Francis gave the walker a good thumping for what he did to his sister.'

After draining our pints we go out into the October light. We walk slowly up the track - our boots crunching on the cinders - stopping to inspect the allotments. A grand row of leeks here, sprouts coming on there. Then past funny little Stan, rattling his tin of peas at his circling pigeons, shouting out, 'Howway ya buggers, get thee sens in!' Then between Tom's muck heaps - built up with railway sleepers - and into his hut.

I sniff, then breathe in whiffs of fresh sawdust, oats, bran and sweet hay, all spiced with the tang of rabbits. "Aye aye." I sigh a bit. "You can't beat the smell of a well-kept rabbit hut."

"Sit yourself on that stool, Bill," Tom says, as he spreads his backside across a feed bin.

"Have you seen this youth?" He points to a Belgian Hare buck, then opens the hutch to reach in. His stubby fingers pick up the rabbit and gently lift him out. He puts the buck onto the grooming bench so that it can move about. As it hops forward, its body quivers and the coppery coat flashes like fire in the sun-shine that comes through the cobwebbed window. "Have you enough light there, Bill? I leave a few spider webs to keep a check on the flies."

I say, "By heck! Yon's a beauty; look at the way he holds himself - and that grand colour. You'll clear the decks wi' that youth when you start showing him. I doubt if I'll ever see a Belgian so fit."

"Well - I was going to pack them in, but then he turned up in a litter of four. I was thinking of building up the Blue Beverens; but now he's come, I'll be running the Hares on a bit longer. You can have a

24

mating off him - after he's been shown."

We sit for a while, quiet, with the door open so that the pipe smoke won't make the rabbits sneeze. Then Tom pulls his watch out of his waistcoat pocket and looks at the time. He twists around, rummages under a pile of Hessian sacks, and pulls one out from the bottom. "Here it is. I'll get a spade."

An hour later sees us on the high moor. We're thick round the middle now, so we stand on the crag breathing hard. Lumley's Farm is far below.

"By! I'm lathered like a hoss from that climb," Tom gasps.

Side by side we take in the cool air.

"This will do," we agree. He digs among the heather roots while I gather up rocks. Then he spreads a square of green velvet in the hole. "This is just a scrap that's been in the wife's remnant drawer for years. Take her out of the sack, Bill." I notice a slight crack in his voice.

"There now... there now." My pal sets the lass carefully on the green velvet and smoothes down the one clump of auburn hair - a curl springs back and flashes red and gold.

We build a cairn over the spot - it's three foot tall. We stand in our polished boots for a bit, caps in hands - thinking.

We blow our noses hard then say to each other, "Aye, that'll be reet," and make our way home.

*Harry Nicholson*

# Wild Gatherings

## The Curlews' Call

Today I trudged over naked moor
And heard the curlews call.
They showered their archaic babble down,
By ling and dry-stone wall.

I thrilled to hear their ancient cries,
A joyous, eerie sound,
Come tumbling, like a benison,
On me, beneath, earthbound.

My spirits soared, I felt alive,
To hear those wild birds sing.
It fevered me with humble hope,
To live another Spring.

Of all the sounds that fill my world
There's none makes my heart stir,
As the curlews' whaup, on wide, wild moor,
When springtime's in the air.

*Ainsley*

# Wagtail

Where do you rush to Dolly Wagtail
With your hat upon three hairs
Do you go to the shops
For the groceries
Without a bag in your hand?

I'm just bobbing along the shore
If you please
Just for a little look
To see what's on the strand today
It's all free you see
No need to pay.

I find all sorts
On this bit of sand
You never know your luck
A nice fat midge and a worm or two
A caddis fly and a pillercat
It's amazing what's to be had
All sorts of things to be had.

*Harry Nicholson*

# Goose Steps

The raiders came in dark of night,
Their stealth a silent game.
Few stood a chance, had time for flight,
Alarmed and scattered, frightened, maimed,
Such little time, the geese all slain.

One goose though, braved all and flew
Into the dark cold night
And made his way through field and wood,
Not turning left or right.
As dawn approached, still filled with fright
He sheltered 'neath a hedge.
Where should he go, what could he do?
There seemed no end in sight.

Unused to fending for himself
He had to find a way.
Perk up you goose. He gave a sigh,
If only he had learned to fly,
He'd join that flock of noisy geese
There, yonder in the sky.
They must be going somewhere;
He'd track the way they went.
Footsore and tired, hungry too,
He waddled on, without a clue,
Then, stopped and gawped as into view
His eyes beheld a wondrous sight.

He shook his head and beat his wings,
His nightmare quite forgotten.
Here was a lake so vast and deep,
His goose steps he did hasten.
With joy he cackled as he ran
Down to the water's edge.
Goose friends were there from round the world
From over distant oceans.
Reprieved and safe, his joy unfurled,
He joined the celebration.

*Pat Henderson*

# On Danby Station
## (Esk Valley Line)

Across the line a Monkey-puzzle tree
Reaches skyward, straight-trunked
Sentinel, sacred Araucanian.
Reptilian branches swoop in curves,
Sharp-scaled leaves, dagger-tipped,
Tough crunching for the Dinosaur.

A hundred years, it measured time:
Rumbling trains called, and carried
Children to school, shepherds to war.
May it watch a thousand more,
Ringing records of climate's change,
Whose parent in *Discovery's* hold
Crossed southern seas from a land
Where no monkey climbed,
Only Andean fire and soft snowfall,
While a close relation, long extinct,
Lies buried, jet-black,
Deep in this Northern shore.

A carriage halts beside the lowest bough.
Two faces, puzzled by the snaking arm,
Twist and crane, striving to see it all.

*Jenny Burgoyne*

*Photo:*
*A Bowes*

# A Long Life

## *The Story of a Tree*

The gnarled tree was ancient, perhaps nearing four centuries old. It had eagerly soaked up the rain and sunshine from well over three hundred summers. Through years, good, bad or indifferent, the tree had efficiently used what precious solar energy it could glean to grow and sink its powerful roots deeper into the rich, nourishing earth, to swell its girth and spread its now mighty limbs outwards and upwards towards the open sky. Every spring and summer it had dressed itself in a dense cloak of rich green leaves. Each year, when autumn came, it bestowed its bountiful seeds to the willing wind. Annually its verdant dress, chameleon-like, faded from green through autumn colours of pale yellow and orange to deep russet and then dead brown. Birds and other wild animals had used it as a permanent home or temporary staging-post. A profusion of insects had thrived in its many holes, cracks and crannies.

Over the years countless children had played in its tangled branches and swung from suspended knotted ropes that they had perilously fastened to its sturdy outstretched lower limbs. In autumns past steaming horse teams led by lone ploughmen had passed back and forth each year beneath the tree's huge shadow, turning over the fecund fields, leaving them laid out like dark swathes of rich brown corduroy. The earth-burnished ploughshares shone like silver fish. Raucous seagulls, screeching and wheeling above in anticipation of a bountiful meal, eagerly followed the plough. Nowadays, noisy, fume-belching powerful tractors had replaced the outmoded heavy horses, although the knowing gulls always returned to scavenge for food exposed by the newly-turned earth.

Young lovers, sauntering along the narrow overgrown path at the edge of the field on a warm summer evening, had tarried in the tree's intimate shade. They leaned against its mighty bole, kissing each other tenderly, oblivious to the summer sun sinking slowly below the distant blue-hilled horizon. The young man had crudely carved their initials into the tree's skin, leaving a permanent surface scar, a heart-shaped wooden tattoo, a lover's token that had outlived its creator. In the evening the luscious smell of hedge woodbine sweetened the air. As the sun went down, small animals took refuge and slept in the safety of the tree's protective arms. In the dead of night, a foraging dog-fox silently slinked by, leaving his unmistakable pungent feral scent as a territorial marker. A fat owl hooted from the tree's uppermost branches, a haunting signal to its far-off mate, whose eerie reply came floating across the empty fields like an ethereal echo. Cold, silvery light from a myriad of moons had cast the tree's substantial ghostly shadow over the peaceful farmland. Without a sound, the noble tree deeply breathed in carbon dioxide and exhaled purifying oxygen into the atmosphere, the vital stuff of life for all living things.

Each winter the tree had been stripped of its leafy mantle by the savage north winds that laid bare its limbs and torso, recklessly scattering the last remnants of the tree's tattered cloak far and wide. With its huge carbuncled feet firmly planted on Mother Earth, naked arms outstretched, head held high, the old tree had embraced and endured the full force of countless icy winter blasts. It had thirsted in times of severe summer drought and struggled in bad years to survive. But the robust tree was a survivor; it had stood its ground, steadfast and immovable.

The tree had outlasted numerous monarchs, mere human mortals, kings and queens whose reigns had come and gone, disappearing into dusty history books. The tree had lived since ancient times, passed through the Great Age of Enlightenment and tasted the polluted air created by the industrial revolution. It had seen the dawn of the modern age with its steam engines, electricity, radios, motorcars, nuclear weapons, jet aeroplanes, television, mobile phones, computers, satellites and space travel. Men had walked on the moon. The tree had lived through troubled times when slaughtered millions of the common people had died in numberless savage wars and conflicts.

But now the tree itself was old and infirm, its body and limbs weakened with the passing of the ages. Pollution and global warming had resulted in an increasingly hostile environment that had played its inimical part. Even the mighty tree was mortal and must in time succumb to old age and decrepitude, as with all living things. Its remarkable long life was nearly done. Nothing living escapes Old Father Time; the Grim Reaper takes all, eventually.

The vicious storm came suddenly in the early hours of the morning and angrily raged about the swaying tree. Forked lightning bolts flashed from the turbulent lead-grey sky followed immediately by claps of outrageous thunder. Continuous rain sluiced down and lay in shimmering sheets on the surface of the waterlogged fields. The peaty waters in the many streams, fords and becks sprang up, gurgling and swishing wildly through ravines and valleys, hurtling under bridges, cascading over rocky falls and weirs, violently scouring the banks of the waterways in a reckless headlong race, as though fleeing from the eye of the storm in panic in a frantic escape to the flooding river and then on to the safe embrace of the distant sea. The raging wind roared like a wild thing.

A blinding lightning flash struck at the heart of the old tree. Angry flames, spraying sparks, swirling smoke and steam exploded from the heart of its bole with the phenomenal natural energy of the electrical strike, like a colossal firework display. There was a sharp crack like the sound of a single rifle shot. For a moment, the stricken tree remained erect, then stately as if in slow motion, gracefully toppled over and crashed, almost without sound, into the wet softness of the ploughed field. Branches cracked and snapped off as the doomed tree thudded into the muddy, water-logged earth. The ancient tree that had proudly stood its ground for centuries was now laid low, its back broken, a dead giant of nature. No one was witness to its demise. The uncaring storm raged on relentlessly throughout the rest of the day, finally blowing itself out with a whimper when evening came. Eventually, the thunder rumbled away into the distance and the incessant rain finally ceased. The sky lightened and calm returned once more to the storm-ravaged countryside.

Next day, the old farmer came and stood beside the fallen tree. He was dwarfed by the enormous bulk of the felled giant. He removed his flat cap as though in reverence to the dead doyen. He rubbed the back of his forearm along his furrowed brow. For as far back as he could recall the tree had stood there. For as long as he could remember he had known the tree. As a little boy, he too had played around the base of the tree and climbed into its lofty branches. He had grown up with the silent sentinel always standing guard. Even the usually stoical farmer was somewhat bereft. He was shaken and felt he had lost a dear old friend. He lingered there for a while in sombre silence before calling his dog to heel. He turned and plodded wearily home, ineffably saddened.

Over the coming months following the storm, the old farmer made regular trips with his tractor and trailer to the stricken tree. The rasping sound of a chain saw, buzzing like a frantic entrapped wasp, could be heard drifting across the open fields as he cut up the hefty limbs of the fallen tree into logs. His wood store soon bulged with the remains of the old tree, precious fuel that would ensure warmth throughout the harsh winter for the farmer and his family. All that remained in the field was the huge horizontal bole of the tree, lying like the prostrate body of some extinct prehistoric behemoth. The tree trunk would be sold to a local sawmill and eventually removed by the timber merchant with the use of specialist gear, a mammoth task. At the mill it would be selectively sawn into rough planking, carefully stored and seasoned for many years, and, in time, sold on at greatly added value as English hardwood for the making of fine furniture and other quality wooden goods and implements.

When the inevitable freezing cold and snows of winter came, the farmer constantly burned the wood from his store to heat his home. On icy winter evenings, after a hard day's work in the fields, he sat with his taciturn wife and old dog around a blazing open fire and enjoyed the warming comfort of the burning logs. Bit by bit, the energy entrapped and sequestered by the old tree from countless summer suns of centuries past was released, as if by magic, as shining heat from the fire. The old ruddy-cheeked farmer dozed by the fire's soporific glow and dreamt he was a child again climbing high up into the branches of the old tree and watching from his lofty viewpoint his father and the team of plodding horses plough and sow the land, land that his grandfather and his father before him had in turn also tilled. It was the same land that the old farmer himself had spent a lifetime cultivating and wresting a hard living from.

Come the following spring, the farmer's stockpile of wood had greatly diminished. The passing of another year would see it completely gone, devoured by the insatiable flames of the hungry farmhouse fires and stoves, gone up in smoke, dust unto dust.

In time, a team of workmen from the sawmill came and unceremoniously removed the massive tree bole from the field with their heavy machinery. The farmer was once again able to plough and sow his land unimpeded by the carcass of the fallen giant. There was now nothing remaining of the venerable tree, except the huge, deep-rooted stump, like an old discarded leather boot, standing in the hedge-line at the side of the field. The stump had been ignominiously trimmed down to hedge level, revealing its annual growth rings that marked off each single year like a living calendar, its life-lines clearly visible for a short time on the cleanly-sawn, flat table-like surface.

By the side of the path in the hedgerow, a little way from the decaying stump, a tiny air-borne seed from the old tree had randomly fallen.  A young sapling had tenaciously taken root and was struggling to stretch its tender incipient shoots skywards: Nature's mysterious and inexorable life-force was at work.  Another age was beginning.

*Ainsley*

## Rabbit

Rabbit in the morning:
astonished and shivering.
Twelve-week old nose,
wide, wide eyes,
delighted legs dithering.

Rabbit in the evening:
Scar-faced buck,
six winters shivering.
One yellowed eye
watches the sky;
old legs quivering.

*Harry Nicholson*

## To the Esk

Your new life splurges forth from deep within
   the bowels of the black and peaty earth
      and springs into a sparkling splashing stream
         to celebrate the rapture of your birth.

Now pushing, gushing, rushing on your way
   past spiky sieves and bracken's arching fronds
      beneath a mountain ash or lonely pine
         with swathes of ancient heather far beyond.

You tumble, rumble on through hills and dales
   your strength increasing as you rush along,
      splashing, crashing over rocks and stones
         your current now is powerful and strong.

But then you leave the craggy ghylls and vales,
   much deeper now and wider as you flow
      so majestically along your chosen course,
         still knowing there are several miles to go.

At last, the briny air drifts ever closer
   and you know you've almost reached your journey's end.
      The long awaited meeting is upon you
         and the mighty sea embraces a new friend.

*Ann Bowes*

## The Hare

The graceful hare so mystical and still
Her backward glance the only movement shown,
Sits waiting, watching at the distant hill,
Daily vigil, hours unfurl.

Those long fine ears that twitch from time to time,
Pop-eyed expression like a human frown,
Alert, athletic, young and in her prime,
Old age for her will never come.

She is disturbed, her lean neck arched in fear,
Brown fur shifting, stirring, constantly at war.
Inborn she knows a predator draws near,
Nerves racing, flowing as in spate.

Long-limbed and powerful, ready for the chase,
Can she outwit her enemies around?
It takes a speedy hound to match her pace,
Vigilant with eyes that never close.

Death is postponed for just a little while,
Sheer strength and pace have shaken off the foe,
Instilled in her an instinct to survive,
Taut muscles give, heart slows.

Alive she kicks and sprints, her spirit high,
On heather hill or stubble she remains,
Wild elegance, the hare will leap with joy,
Exuberance, her energy ignites.

Will mystic powers give her another day?
Her startled stare will gaze upon the moon,
Created in such beauty — no escape,
So short a life for one who cannot win.

*Julia Organ*

*Illustration: H Walker*

# Home Brew

## Sunshine After Rain

The love of my life thinks he is going to leave me for another woman.

Well… he isn't.

I press my face deep into his thick, black woolly jumper. It is loosely knit with a high collar which frames his handsome face and makes him appear even taller. I know it is loosely knit because I knitted it for him myself. I want him to be cosy in the winter weather. The sweater feels chunky and familiar, a comforting mix of aftershave and warmth. I feel his arms tighten around me and I relax and inhale. I hold him as tight as I can. I don't want to ever let him go. He is part of me and I him. His infatuation will end and then he will want me again. I shall make him see that but I have to be careful. He brushes my hair with his lips and rests his chin on the top of my head. I try not to but I read a lot into that little gesture.

I smile. She doesn't stand a chance. Not really. We have history.
As I stand in the sacred circle of his arms, my mind wanders back through the years we have spent together. It is the smell of him that I miss when he isn't there. Involuntarily I take another deep breath and fill my lungs with the irreplaceable scent of him. I need to store it away for later, for when he has left me, although I know deep down he won't leave. The thought is preposterous. But, if he does, I can curl up, close my eyes, take his aroma out of my stash of memories and smell him again. And remember him exactly as he is now. Tall, perfect, beautiful.

He jabs me playfully in the ribs, interrupting my agonised adoration of him. My eyes shoot open and I turn them up to look into his concerned face.

He can only guess at the pain hidden behind my eyes and the scheming and the tearing concentration of grief. He does not know anything of the dreadful thoughts I harbour or the plots I am hatching to keep him. He believes me when I tell him that I am finally okay with everything and understand that he needs to move on.

"Come on you. We can't stand here all day."

'Why not?' screams the voice in my head. 'Why not?'

But I know better than to show my pain. I have tried that before and it doesn't work. He withdraws from me. He puts up barriers and becomes secretive. I have to be clever. I have to be cleverer than her. I force a smile and I hope it does not look anything other than genuine.

'Just get rid of her. That's all you need to do. Stay with me. She can't love you like I do.'

"Yes," I say out loud. "Let's go. There's a lot to do."

I make myself stand proud, shoulders back. I don't want him thinking I am pathetic. Although I am not above using that if all else fails. For the moment, however, I want to show him that I am strong and dependable, someone to be proud of, happy to look after him. Then he won't leave me.

Reluctantly, I loosen my hold on him. I want to stand beside him forever, loving him. It is my job. It is all I have ever wanted to do or so it seems right now. Life plays some mean tricks. This perfect man doesn't want me anymore. He doesn't need me. He has found someone younger and prettier. Oh, the agony of it!

There was a time when he would sit and watch me whilst I got ready to go out. He would tell me lovingly how pretty I was and stroke my hair. He used to take an interest in what I was wearing and tell me I was beautiful. He thinks that she is beautiful now. I watched them together the other day. They didn't know I was there. His face wore the same expression when he looked at her as it used to when he looked at me. He used to love looking at me. I used to bask in it. Now he loves looking at her. I can't bear it and want to do something nasty to her. Jealousy is destructive and it is eating me alive.

I have been very angry but now I am calm. She can't have him. She is not good for him, and, anyway, he is mine. The sooner she accepts that the better. Guiltily I glance up at him.

'Love ME! Choose ME!'

"Come on," he says, anxiously stroking my back, sensing my sadness. "Come on. Look. There's time for a walk. Let's go."

He grabs my hand and yanks me along behind him. He is strong and handsome. I have always thought so. We walk for a mile or so, chatting amiably, as though he is not about to leave me for another woman. He laughs back over his shoulder at me. His long legs make effortless strides through the wet grass, making it impossible for me to keep up without breaking into a little half-trot. Despite the cloying feeling of loss that I am battling, I laugh back at him. God, I love him. Even now whilst in an agony of jealousy I love him. I would do anything to keep him.

'How can you leave me?' screams the treacherous little voice.

"C'mon slow coach. Race you home." I yell this at him, trying to be the fun person that once was the centre of his world. I force myself to laugh with him.

Pushing him over in the long grass, I start to run. Soon I can hear him pounding up behind me and I squeal as he grabs me round the waist and pulls me down beside him. We lie there fighting to catch our breath and grinning up into the sky. He isn't going to leave me. How can he leave me? We love each other.

He grows suddenly serious. "It's been great you know. All these years have been fantastic but it is time. I can't believe I am leaving you behind."

I try to smile but this time I fail. I can't believe it either and there is nothing I can think of to say. I feel my eyes fill up.

'Why wasn't I enough?' I want to ask this. But I don't.

Instead I swallow hard, throat tight, eyes prickling. It would be so easy to cry.

"We've talked about this, darling," I say stoutly, "You have to follow your heart. Our time together is over… I know that."

But it is brave talk. And I can see out of the corner of my eye that my darling is breathing a sigh of relief that I am not going to make a scene.

If only I could see what he sees in her, it might help. Oh, I know she is quite pretty but she does not know how he likes things done. Does she know that he loves brown sauce on his bacon sandwich? Does she know how his clothes need to be folded? Does she know he loses his car keys every time he walks through the door? Or that they are always to be found in his jacket pocket, even though he left them on the shelf? Does she know he is biologically incapable of unloading a dishwasher?

"Darling, there's a bottle of your favourite wine in the fridge. Shall we go home and have a glass? It might help you relax." I look at him almost flirtatiously from under my lashes.

"It's a bit early for me, poppet. Anyway, I need my wits about me today." He gives me a knowing look, "Trying to get me drunk?"

I put my arm through his and give it a squeeze. He covers my hand with his and looks deep into my eyes. He holds my gaze because I find it impossible to turn away from him, as ever.

"You have been amazing about this. I can't tell you how much I admire you. I know it hasn't been easy."

"Oh, think nothing of it, darling. When faced with the inevitable…"

We both stop and stare as a flock of geese fly low over our heads in formation. It is an impressive sight. We can feel their wings beating their tattoo. Twenty or more birds, majestic and dignified, fly unflinchingly towards the horizon. I wish that we could tag on the end and fly away together to a new life.

We look at each other, and I think briefly that he is thinking the same thing and my heart soars like the birds above us. He holds my gaze for a couple of seconds, then takes a deep breath.

Reluctantly he says, "We need to go home now, darling. I have to get sorted."

The fire is still burning snappily in the grate when we arrive back home. We shiver from the shock of stepping from the drizzly, cold outdoors into the warmth of the house.

"I think it's time we got ready."

I nod, not trusting myself to speak. The moment I never thought would come is almost here. I dash from the room and up the stairs. I sit in front of the mirror and think for a little while. Then I force myself to stand up and I walk across the bedroom to my wardrobe.

It's over.

"Are you ready, poppet?" I can hear him shouting from the bottom of the stairs. "I'm leaving… with or without you!"

I take a huge slug of air and try to stop myself shaking. "Yes. Ready. I'm coming." And off I go.

I open the bedroom door and walk with leaden legs along the landing to the top of the stairs. I pause and look down. Again I think I am going to cry but I don't. No, I don't cry. I smile. I smile a huge watery smile. It feels like sunshine after the rain. There he is smiling back up at me. I can see in his eyes that he thinks I am beautiful. He is looking at me in exactly the same way as he looked at me when he was six years old, sitting stroking my hair in front of my bedroom mirror whilst I got ready to go out.

"Mum you look amazing." And I know that he means it. And I know that I won't lose him. And I know that he will always love me.

I know that he and I will arrive at the church together. We will walk in, arm in arm, supporting each other as we always have. I know that his young and lovely bride will look divine, and I know that I will grow to love her. And I know that this day will be wonderful.

Outside the sun is shining on a freshly washed world and suddenly… I just know.

*Hilary Walker*

## Merely by Chance

Jess Harris, a young girl in her late teens, pushed open the brown painted gate onto the station platform, let it clang shut behind her and made her way toward the ticket office. She wore a navy anorak, faded jeans and sensible brown shoes that had seen better days. Her honey-coloured hair was tied back revealing her pretty but tear-stained face. Finding no one in attendance she dumped her bulging hold-all on the floor and made her way round to the waiting room where she could hear someone whistling. A cheery, overweight gentleman, attired in navy uniform was sweeping the floor. He smiled as the young girl entered.

"Evening miss. Can I help you?"

"I need to buy a ticket for the last train." The smile left the man's face.

"Last train? You're a bit late for that miss. It left half an hour ago," he said. The young girl looked crestfallen.

"But it says 9.50 on my timetable and it's only a quarter to nine."

"Oh, you must have the summer one."

"But it's only September."

"Exactly. Changes on the first. There're no more trains today, miss." With head down and shoulders sagging, she turned to go. Feeling sorry for this young girl the man called after her.

"I'm almost done here. Can I give you a lift somewhere?" The girl turned briefly.

"No, it's all right, thank you. I've got friends in the village," she lied. Retrieving her hold-all, she hurried out of the station. The dim

42

streetlights lit the way as she took the road leading out of the village. By the last streetlamp she found a seat near a small lake and stopped to ponder on her situation. With nowhere to stay and only enough money for her ticket back to Leeds, Jess was feeling desolate and lonely.

Jess left the city that morning in such high spirits, her apprehension and excitement mounting as the journey passed. After alighting from the train she made light of the two mile walk to the next village of Benford where her inquiries as to the whereabouts of the local blacksmith, Joss Sanderson, were soon answered. She felt nervous when she finally arrived. She walked towards the front of the house, passing the large wrought-iron notice that read, 'Benford Forge, Farrier and Blacksmith'.

She heard the loud clang of hammer on metal and from somewhere behind the main house a horse whinnied loudly. As she approached the front door a small black and white terrier appeared, barking excitedly, bringing a young girl, a few years younger than Jess, from the house. She was a well-built girl with a crop of short black hair and thick fringe. She smiled as she approached Jess.

"Can I help you? Quiet, Topsy," she scolded the noisy terrier. "Sorry. Did you want to see my father?"

"No. I hope I've come to the right house. I'm looking for someone called Margaret Sanderson," Tess said. The smile disappeared as the young girl's face clouded over.

"You've come to the right house but why do you want to see Margaret Sanderson?"

"Well..." Jess hesitated, her heart pounding within her. She had gone over several times in her mind what she would say. "I know this lady in Leeds who knew Margaret several years ago. I was asked to look her up if I was ever visiting this way," she smiled. The young girl was silent as she stared out across the hills beyond the village. Eventually she turned back to Jess, her young face etched with sadness.

"I'm afraid my mother died two years ago," she said. Jess reeled and paled visibly. This couldn't be true. Not now, not after all this time. Eventually, she managed to speak.

"Margaret Sanderson was your mother?" she stammered. "And she's dead?" Before the young girl could answer a man's voice bellowed out from the buildings.

43

"Meg, where's that mug of tea?" The young girl glanced towards the buildings.

"I'm sorry, I'll have to go. Dad gets very impatient for his tea when he's shoeing. I'm sorry if you've had a wasted journey." She was about to turn and go when, unable to stop herself, Jess flung her arms round the young girl, tears welling in her eyes.

"I'm so very sorry about your mother." And turning blindly she picked up her hold-all and walked away. She could no longer contain the emotion within her. The tears poured down her cheeks as her faltering steps took her away from the forge.

As Jess sat on the bench all alone she thought how cruel life could be. Things had been bad before but now they seemed infinitely worse. All her hopes and dreams had been shattered and the planning that had gone into this visit over the last six months had been in vain. She would have to return to Leeds and Aunt Ellie, her foster mother, who had helped her so much with her search. Sadly, Aunt Ellie, not really her aunt, had been diagnosed with cancer and was soon to go and live with her daughter where she would be well cared for. Jess knew when that day came she would be sent back to the children's home. She had spent most of her early childhood there, apart from brief spells with various foster parents, and hated the place. After experiencing a reasonably happy time with Aunt Ellie she was even more loathe to return to the home.

A light rain was beginning to fall, dimpling the still waters of the lake. It was getting late and realising she could not stay on the bench all night Jess picked up her bag once more and set off down the darkening road, away from the village.

After trudging wearily for about half a mile she came to a lane end with a sign carved on a huge stone 'Greenend Farm'. Jess could see the distant lights shining from the farmhouse, welcoming lights. There would be barns and hay sheds. Perhaps the owners would let her stay there, just until the morning. The light drizzle was now a steady rainfall and the lure of somewhere warm and dry to sleep was too much for Jess. She turned into the gateway and slowly made her way up the lane.

As she neared the farmhouse she was tempted to find a cosy corner in a building and curl up and go to sleep, putting the cruel world behind her. The barking of a farm dog soon put paid to that idea. She approached the door of the house and raised the large brass knocker.

Trying to hide her surprise and curiosity, the attractive farmer's wife who answered the door, greeted Jess warmly.

"Come in, out of the rain. Have you broken down?" Jess stepped inside the large porch which seemed to be full of coats, wellington boots, trainers and dog bowls.

"No." Jess was too tired to invent a story so blurted out the truth. "I'm sorry to trouble you so late at night but I've missed the last train home and have no money for lodgings. I saw the lights and was wondering if I could rest up in a barn or somewhere for the night." Jan Golding, a hard working, kind-hearted mother of three young teenage boys, took in the tired dejected demeanour of the young girl standing before her. She noted, too, the damp shabby clothes and battered luggage and it was not only her curiosity that impelled her to offer hospitality to the unexpected visitor.

"I'm sure we can do better than that. Give me your coat and let's go inside. Have you eaten recently?"

"I had a sandwich on the train coming," Jess replied, as she followed the woman into a warm, welcoming kitchen.

"I imagine you could do with a clean up and some dry clothes. Have you got other clothes with you?" she asked, as she hung the damp jacket over a chair.

"Yes, in my bag but I didn't want to put you out at all."

"Nonsense, dear. I bet you could do with a nice hot bath while I fix you some supper." Jan was no fool and with three boys was quite used to teenage problems but she sensed this young woman was facing a serious difficulty. Jess was too tired to refuse the kindness offered and, picking up her bag, meekly followed Jan into a warm spacious bathroom. After running a hot bath and laying out towels Jan left her guest and went in search of her husband, Paul. The present incident did not surprise him. Usually it was stray cats, lost dogs or injured birds that his wife rescued.

"I haven't asked her anything yet but she seems very distressed about something. I'm sure she's been crying. I'll give her a bed for the night, of course. We can't have her sleeping in the barn. She can have John's room – he won't be back 'til Sunday."

Later, after Jess had managed to eat a bowl of beef stew and crusty roll, Jan made a pot of tea and shouted Paul through to join them. She was most surprised at his reaction when he saw the young woman. He stared at the stranger in disbelief and after a brief greeting drank his tea in silence.

An hour later, with Jess tucked up in bed, Jan rejoined Paul. He was staring into the fire but looked up as his wife entered the room.

"You've been a long time," he said.

"I've never heard such a sad story." She flopped onto the sofa next to him. "The poor girl opened her heart out. She had me almost in tears, too."

"Did you find out her name?"

"Yes, she's called Jess Harris and..." before she could continue Paul interrupted her.

"I knew it as soon as I saw her. She has to be the daughter of Margaret Harris. Same coloured hair, same eyes, same..."

"You knew this Margaret then?"

"Yes, several years ago. I heard through a mutual friend about ten years back that she had returned to the area. She came to Benford with her husband and little girl. I actually bumped into her a few years ago at the General Hospital. It was when I had that prostate scare and she was working there as a nurse. At first she didn't seem to recognize me, which I thought rather strange."

"Why? Did you know her well?" Jan asked, with a woman's natural curiosity. Paul gave his wife a sheepish grin.

"Yes, rather. She was my first big love. She was 18 and I was 22 but she was far more worldly wise than I was. I thought she'd broken my heart when, after six weeks, she suddenly left home to work in Leeds without giving me any explanation. Now I think I know why." Jan stared at him in disbelief.

"You don't mean..." her voice tailed off.

"Yes. I've been sitting here working it all out. What did she tell you?"

"She knows that she was put in a home shortly after her birth. It has only been in recent years, since she was fostered by this Aunt Ellie, that she had managed to trace her mother; only she was two years too late. No wonder the poor girl was broken. She sobbed her heart out to me upstairs. I've never felt so helpless." Paul reached across and squeezed his wife's hand.

"Well, we may be able to change that. I think I know now why Margaret left so suddenly to work in Leeds. Jess may have lost the mother she never knew but, merely by chance, I believe she has found her father, whom I hope she will come to know and love. And you will have the daughter you always wanted."

*Ann Bowes*

# Things to Remember

The bag is old, out of shape, with scuff and black drag marks on the base and sides. As I pulled it from the cupboard it flopped open ready to receive whatever I wished to put in it. I want to do this alone. I am the only one who knows what is important to me and what is of no consequence. The only person likely to know what I really value has been gone for some time and I'm not sure how much of me as a woman my children really know. No, I'll do this for myself.

What to take? That's the thing. My clothes and shoes have gone – well, the best of them. I won't need old gardening clothes or painting shirts, though I've not worn those since the last fall, truth to tell, but I've taken some old things as I rather enjoy being scruffy. I'm certainly not one to be dolled in pearls for afternoon tea. I hope they don't expect that. Disappointment ahead if they do. I suppose I can always stay in my room if I don't like it. I'll have a lovely view of the sea with plenty of light. That was what swung it really. If they'd shown me a dingy place or a cold north-facing room I'd have stayed here and taken my chances. But I loved the view and I loved the light so I signed the agreement and that was it really.

I can't get my big painting in the bag, and I'm not going if I can't take that. It's very large and it isn't even our dog but it's so like him it gives me goose bumps and I can almost feel the thick waves of hair under his throat when I look at it. There were lots of times when that old lad kept me sane. On call, whatever the hour, he would always be there to welcome me, even if it was only the wag of a tail as I passed on my way to bed. He'd take a walk whatever the time and, if the kids were playing up or I was struggling in the early days of John's illness, he'd trot round and about me down the lane only returning to sniff my hand when he heard me crying. There have been lots of times since then when I've put my hand out when I've been sitting on the sofa half expecting to feel his rough curls under my fingers. I couldn't have another, not now, but I'd have loved to have gone and chosen another golden pup, but no, the painting will have to suffice. Brown paper and string should do it.

The tin of photographs will fit in the end of the case and the book the three of them made for us on our silver anniversary, of course. 'This is your life,' they said proudly and gave us their selection of snaps from our early years. Our history, theirs too. I don't know if our choice of pictures would have been the same as theirs. There's no sign of the chaos, the fatigue, the struggle to do what was needed and do my job as well, at a time when a career was not supposed to matter for a woman. I'm relieved now that they never censure me or feel aggrieved at all the times I was missing. I'd have done it just the same, I'm afraid. I'm ashamed of my selfish streak but I so enjoyed going my own way and loved the work I did - the involvement in other lives. Sometimes when I look at my children they seem older than I am, more staid. I suppose it's because my head stopped in about my twenty fifth year although the poor old body ticked on and is now showing its years even though it has served me well. Life's reverses are strange. It's now they who struggle with the strong wills of their children whilst I sit back and cheer the youngsters on. I slip all the grandkids a few pounds to eke out loans, for Saturday nights, trainers they must have or new shoes and guitar strings. It's worth it to see the smile on their faces and it buys me confidences. Mad Granny B they call me and I like it, truth to tell. They tell me all sorts of secrets and I love the different shades of them, the different characters. Chloe, the one who'd have driven me demented if she'd been mine, is the one I hope to live to see grow into her own skin. She'll create smoke, that one, and no doubt there'll be ructions ahead, but I have a sofa bed in my new place so I can still provide a bolt hole when any of them need it - I made sure of that.

So the photos go in.

Books. Oh dear, how can I leave all these. Apart from a few treasured stories it's the poetry I'll take and the battered thesaurus and the dictionary. No doubt I'll be doing more crosswords than ever now; I shan't be occupied in the house. My two girls bought me the best poetry book and it was such a lovely surprise. It wasn't just the book itself, more the fact that they'd actually put thought into the choice and that they knew me well enough to choose something I'd have bought for myself. They've said they'll keep a big bookcase in the downstairs hall, even after the house is altered and I can leave my collection in there. Maybe they want to keep the books so that they can then read them too? I don't think so! Although Jill will find time. The other two certainly won't. Rosie's too busy and James only relaxes with things you can throw, hit, catch or ride, so he won't be dipping in and out of books for consolation – not yet, anyway. Now music. Another problem. To look at me now, even on a good day, you'd never guess that I've shimmied with the best of them. I was

48

already over the hill when Guy Mitchell came up with 'She wears red feathers and a hula hula skirt' but John still thought that one suited my style!  Bless him!  I don't know what he'd have thought now if he could see my copies of the Beatles, Hot Chocolate, the Stones and so on, slotted in with his Chopin and the Villa Lobos that still stirs my soul.  I find they remind me of the days when World War Three threatened to break out upstairs and all three kids turned up the volume on their stereos.  World War Three.  We all worried about it but it hasn't happened so far, even though we've been close.  I'll leave out World War Two.  It passed in dark places, terrible wounds, shattered lives and hours and hours of dirty work and back-breaking study.  The later years were better, though I enjoyed the camaraderie of St George's and the thrill of walking home in the blackout with that nice Canadian boy.  Better not mention him either; I find the children shock very easily.

I'll take the stuff I've written, for the children to have after I've gone, and all the family stuff too - that can go in the bag.  They'll get some surprises.  I don't want to pull them down with sorrows and burst any balloons, but they must know that all of us are human with feet of clay and yet we all still have the strength to cope despite the blows.  I'd like to see their faces when they get the full story!  Jill will learn most because she can read between the lines, especially when she gets her hands on the anthology I started in the Fifth form and still use - I've left it to her for that reason.  The plot of a life in other people's words.  That's the thing about poetry: I'm always astonished to find there's no situation I've ever been in where there isn't a poem that mirrors my feelings at the time.  So I'll need the big book for this next new venture.

I'll take the quilt from across the armchair that Rosie sewed for me when I was sixty; it will tuck in the bag and hold my treasures safely in place until I unpack.  It's like her, all patched with scarlet, coral, ruby, burgundy and every vibrant shade in between.  There's velvet and silk, corduroy and damask and the red fleece lining is soft and warm.  It lifts my heart every time my eye falls on it and reminds me of her softness and generosity whenever I wrap it round me for warmth or just for comfort.  I'll put my lamp into its folds too, the one that stood on the piano with dangling strings of beads fringing the pink glass shade.  That was a retirement gift from the practice and it softens the edges of any room beautifully when the dark encroaches.  I might need that.  I'll put in the big box of truffles James brought last week and the bottle of Courvoisier to weight the bag. Mustn't neglect the inner woman!

I don't need much in the way of ornaments, just the little bear tumbling with his head between his paws that we bought in Falmouth that first year and the pair of white porcelain swans. They've been on every mantelpiece of every house I've ever lived in. One swan has crazed fine cracks all over it. My dad said they got there when his mother allowed them to use the hollow birds to ladle bath water over their heads when they sat in the tub in front of the kitchen fire on bath nights. I've often thought about the two little boys bathed in the warmth of the coal-stoked range with the water gleaming on their bodies. It's a miracle they didn't smash the swans as they are quite delicate with lovely arched necks. I wouldn't let my three anywhere near them; they're much too precious.

It all looks a bit forlorn now I'm ready to go but then I suppose the life's gone out of it for me. Next time I visit this old house it will all be different. The renovations start next week and when it's finished there'll be two homes, one facing the common and the other looking over the river, and two of my three installed with all their various partners, children and partners' children. Rosie, too, will no doubt be drifting in and out of the bottom workshop as she always has. Now the pink light is off, the furniture and curtains look shabby and worn. If I'd stayed I'd have had to decorate but it's not my problem any more.

Funny, though it's sad, I feel relieved too. 'Things' mean less as you get older. I've lived the life I've wanted and now all that does matters, except the people of course, will happily fit in a battered old bag.

The rain has cleared up whilst I've been packing and the sea will be sparkling when I set out my bits of things at Montrosa. They tell me the food's good, there are some nice people living there and the residents go off to the theatre and out for meals. It's just right for walks along the Esplanade.

I think I'll leave the bag here whilst I go upstairs for a last look round. While I'm up there I'll just find those silver sandals I had years ago for James' graduation 'do' and a couple of those scarves in the bureau that John always said made my eyes look brighter; they'll tuck in the top of the bag and, you never know, I might just need them.

*Pat Almond*

# Boy Wanderer

He wasn't sure how long he'd been walking. He had forgotten to pick up his watch before he'd slipped out. The sun had appeared above the horizon as he'd reached the top pasture above the farm and the church clock in the village in the next valley had chimed six times. It was the last day of the holidays and he had to get right away and forget. Tomorrow they would take him back to the shut-in smells of mince and boiled cabbage and the sharp whiff of urine in the dormitory.

His mother would be cross, as usual, that he had gone off without telling her, but he knew that she would waste his day. He would have to help pack and attempt the homework he had avoided all summer. He had waited until she had gone out to the cowshed with a drink for his stepfather. He'd never quite forgiven her for remarrying, even though his father had died while he was still a baby and there had been the farm to run. At school he was 'William', like his father, but his mother always called him Billy. He was her 'Billy Boy'.

Down in the village he managed to skirt round the edge of the houses on the field-paths without being spotted. He didn't want to have to talk to anyone who knew him and explain himself. He had to pass the back of his old school and stopped to look through the railings at the yard where he used to play, but, since he had been sent away, he had lost touch with the local boys. He had always preferred to go off exploring on his own after school and discover hidden places, high in the hills, where he could be alone under the sky and look out across a land where no one else was visible. As a boarder he was confined to the school grounds under constant supervision and at night they were locked in.

He felt unusually tired. The steep pull up from the farm had been a struggle and he wondered if he was coming down with flu or something else which would keep him home a little longer. The morning sun was warm but even earlier he hadn't felt cold. He had got hot with the exertion and felt the sweat running down his neck. He was thirsty but he had brought nothing with him. He was determined to carry on. He longed to reach the foot of The Rocks, his favourite goal, one more time before he had to leave.

He concentrated on placing one foot in front of another as he climbed the field behind the church. He had put on his plimsolls but he realised he was still wearing his pyjama bottoms and more strangely he was wearing a dressing gown, navy-blue, like his school coat. Perhaps it was his stepfather's and he'd picked it up in his hurry to get out. He stopped to catch his breath. He felt in the pocket and found an opened packet of mints. He put three in his mouth, and, as he crunched them, he turned to see the line of the quarry, curving between two crags over to his left.

He pushed on in a renewed effort to reach the ridge although his head and heart continued to pound to the same alarming beat. Was it a fever? His calves ached. He bent over, and, clutching the tussocky grass, he crawled to the crest. He slumped forward and lay outstretched, gasping for air. He rolled onto his back and looked up at the spinning sky until the world came to a halt.

He lifted his head, turned and saw The Rocks, thrusting their fingers above, like the clustered spires of a thousand churches. Between each tower a narrow cleft, no more than a crack, shot straight down into the earth. He imagined finding a way onto those pinnacles. He would step across each gap and look out over the world from his fortress. He had circled the base many times but had found no way to scale the smooth, bare faces of sheer rock. Instead, he had satisfied himself with the view out to the shining strip of sea that shimmered in the distance.

He heard an engine on the rough track that ran in the depression between the ridge where he was sitting and The Rocks above. He stood up and saw a vehicle, yellow and white, below him. A woman got out, shouted and waved. It was his mother. She'd come to fetch him. He started down the path to her. A man suddenly appeared from the driver's side. It wasn't his stepfather but someone in uniform. He was in serious trouble this time.

Half jogging, half stumbling towards her, he called out, "Sorry, Mum!"

She ran to meet him and grabbed him around the waist.

"Oh Dad, I'm not your Mum. I'm Eileen, your daughter. Why do you do it, Dad? I can't have you home for a weekend if you keep going off like this."

The man was gripping his upper arm.

"How is the old boy? His mind wandering?"

"If only his feet didn't follow! I hid his clothes this time, but it's no good. I can't lock him in, can I?"

From the rear seat Billy could see, if he craned his neck, The Rocks, finally disappearing from sight. The shut-in smell like dentist's gas hit the back of his throat. Mince and cabbage and urine. He knew where he was bound.

*Jenny Burgoyne*

*Enamel artwork by Harry Nicholson*

# Rum Sauce

## Arthur and the Loaf of Bread

Now Arthur was a lazy spouse,
He never helped about the house,
A totally idle MCP,
No domesticity O!
No domesticity.

His wife did everything for him,
She would treat him like the Royal King,
And though it rubbed against the grain,
She never did complain O!
Not once did she complain.

Arthur was so indolent,
Never washing up, nor shopping went,
No DIY, no making tea
He struggled to switch on TV,
To turn on the TV.

Alas one day, his wife fell ill,
Her household chores could not fulfil,
They called the doctor to her bed,
"She must have total rest," he said,
"And she must stay in bed."

"O Arthur, darling," sighed his wife,
"I'm sorry to disturb your life,
But as I've got to stay in bed,
Would you go to the corner store O!
Get me a loaf of bread."

So, to make amends to his ailing wife,
(For he knew he'd caused her nowt but strife.)
And despite his shock at her request,
He resolved to do his best,
Go buy the staff of life.

So off he set for the corner store,
A place he'd not been in before,
With purse and bag and note that read –
Just one thing – 'a loaf of bread' O!
A simple loaf of bread.

The shop being full, he stayed outside,
Some may have thought this macho pride,
But the truth be known, the reason why,
Away from home, he was very shy,
Yes, the MCP was shy.

The shop soon cleared, and he stepped in,
The doorbell clanged a terrible din.
Arthur, startled by the noise,
Was fairly knocked clean off his poise,
It knocked him off his poise.

From behind the till, a young girl smiled,
As Arthur to the counter filed,
"Can I help you sir?" with charm she said,
He blurted out, "A loaf of bread, O!
I need a loaf of bread."

"Certainly sir," (a coquettish smile),
"Just follow me; bread's down this aisle."
Her colleague sniggered. He blushed red,
As the girl ushered Arthur to the bread,
The numerous racks of bread.

There, Arthur gawped, with vacant stare,
Scratched his head, stroked his hair,
Such ample choice, it made him frown,
Said the helpful girl, "Is it white or brown?"
"Do you want it white or brown?"

"O give me white," was his weak reply,
She looked at him with tender eyes,
"How would you like your loaf of bread?
Do you want it large or small?" she said.
"Large or small?" she said.

He shook his head, now full of doubt,
"O give me large," he blurted out.
"Sliced or un-sliced? Sir," she said.
Arthur gasped, and clutched his head –
"Just give me a loaf of bread!"

"O! Make it sliced," said Arthur dazed,
His patience spent, his temper raised.
The assistant - trying to hide her grin -
Said, "Is it thick, or is it thin?
The slices thick or thin?"

"Good God! Enough of this!" he said,
"I've changed my mind, forget the bread,
A pound of sausages instead!"
"Will that be pork or beef?" she said,
"Sir, pork or beef?" she said.

He turned and from the store soon fled,
*Sans* sausages, no loaf of bread,
Home to his wife, so ill in bed,
Without his pride, without her bread.
Without her loaf of bread.

*Ainsley*

*This narrative piece, based on a true event,*
*was written as a song to be sung in the folk style.*

# Oomph!

For years I never knew of its existence
But I suppose that it must always have been there -
Waiting in the shadows – patient, silent,
For the day when it could flaunt its 'savoir faire'.

I've no idea where it ever came from,
Some say it is inherent in the genes,
But I never realized that *I* possessed it
Or tried to understand just what it means.

Even now when people tell me that I have it
I expect they mean it's just a load of bumph?
But protesting, say I should be proud to own it
And explaining, simply say that I've got *oomph*!

*Ann Bowes*

# Great Expectations

He planned to impress his internet date,
The blonde with a good sense of humour,
You know what I mean, attractive and slim,
He wished he could meet her much sooner.

But she dithered and pondered, dallied and stalled,
As she weighed up his charm and his wealth.
Could she really be sure he wasn't a bore?
She would hate to be left on the shelf.

They decided to meet and keep it discreet,
The venue a North Yorkshire town.
Expectations were high as she gave a deep sigh
At the thought that he might let her down.

She had lied about age - she had worked on the stage,
Her photo was old and enhanced.
Would he see through her bluff or go off in a huff?
She could easily lose her one chance.

They eventually met, wondering what to expect.
He was captured by her lovely smile,
But she wasn't too sure if she liked what she saw,
He was older by many a mile.

He'd described to the blonde he was handsome and suave.
She thought he was young and carefree.
Imagine her shock - she had to take stock
When she found he was aged ninety-three.

They had both been deceived but felt rather relieved
To find they had not been quite truthful.
Her blonde hair was dyed, her age not supplied,
No wonder they both looked so rueful.

Let a lesson be learnt when your fingers get burnt
And your internet date goes awry,
But these two now agreed, it suited their need
For her eighty-ninth birthday was nigh.

*Julia Organ*

*Illustration: H Walker*

# A Host of Plastic

A Pastiche    *(with apologies to W.W.)*

I sauntered slowly down a track
That winds below the moorland crags,
When all at once I saw a stack,
A mass of tattered plastic bags;
Along the beck, among the trees,
Fluttering and rustling in the breeze.

Continuous as the stars that light
The darkness in the cosmic sphere,
They stretched beyond my furthest sight
Across the waters of the weir:
Ten million saw I in a trance,
Flapping their skirts in frantic dance.

They caught on boughs, to slap and strain
And roar a wild cacophony;
A human could not but feel pain,
In such an insane company:
I watched - and watched - but little thought
What hell the scene to me had brought:

For, when I'm lying on my bed
In empty or in thoughtful state,
They haunt the spaces in my head
And lead the way to nightmare's gate;
And then my heart on horror snags
And thrashes with those plastic bags.

*Jenny Burgoyne*

# A Writer's Dilemma

I wish I was less disciplined
And didn't give a damn
About the jobs that should be done,
The cobwebs, dust and dirty pan.
I will relax, forget the chores
And think of number one.

I'll disappear with pen and pad
To a corner of my hovel.
Never mind the un-ironed clothes,
The empty fridge, the Emin bed,
I think I'll write a novel.
For adult, teen or maybe child?
I chew my pen and shake my head;
I really need a break.
The words won't come, the void is great,
Oh pull yourself together, mate,
You know it's there, just concentrate.

Suddenly, the words appear
And surge across the paper.
I give a smile,
How's this for style!
This writing lark's a caper.

*Pat Henderson*

# Appetite for Work

## Flames

The aerosol clanged as it hit the train tracks twelve feet below him. He carefully pulled himself along the ledge, over the embankment and into the lane. He knew he should not be here. If his care worker saw his tag high up on the bridge his new placing would be at risk, but he did it anyway.

The new couple were good people; he liked them. Sheila had a wicked laugh and could cook, and Dennis was OK. There was no fuss, no earnest talking and they seemed happy he was there, but he knew he was on trial, moved on because the last family 'couldn't control' him.

As he rounded the end of the Avenue he could see blue lights. Ambulance, not police. He ran towards them recognising Dennis.

"It's a perforated appendix they think," said his foster father anxiously. "Come on."

Soon they were screaming into the rear entrance of A and E and Shelia was hurried away for surgery.

By the morning she was in recovery and the man and boy were sharing a pot of tea and a fry up.

"Blimey," said Dennis, "We won't starve then. I didn't know you could cook."

"You pick up all sorts when you move about a bit," Josh said.

"Well, I suppose you would," replied the man thoughtfully.

"You'd better come in to work with me until school starts again."

Josh wasn't sure what 'work' was, only that it took place in a small workshop in the arches near the railway yard. He was surprised to find a brightly lit workroom redolent with the familiar smell of cellulose and adhesive.

"Know anything about vinyls, lad?" said an elderly man laying out drawings on the worktable.

"Not really," said Josh.

"What about computers? We used to do it all by hand you know."

62

"Those days have all but gone Tom," said Dennis overhearing the conversation. "The future lies with lads like Josh and James over there who can set it up for the likes of us."

For several days Josh watched, made tea and ran errands, waiting for his chance. Dennis came and went as Sheila recuperated. His chance came on the third day, when James didn't turn in for work.

"Bad cold his mam said," muttered Tom. "Now what do we do? No James and the boss away to see the missus."

"What's on for today?" Josh asked.

"Some fancy job for that new club opening. They're using a stick-over vinyl to save cash."

"Could I have a go?"

"You can for me lad, just don't cock the machine up or he'll have me retired before you know it!"

Josh eased himself into the seat in front of the screen and opened the programme.

"Don't know what they want really, but they call it 'Flames'," said Tom, moving into the stockroom with an arm full of patterns. Josh was so absorbed in what he was doing that Tom made the tea. As he placed Josh's cup down he glanced across at the screen.

"Good God lad!" he said, "That's a fine and fancy job I must say."

"Love these metallics," said Josh. 'Flames' was picked out in curling tongues of copper, gold and scarlet.

"If I'd more time I could make a real job of it," Josh said, "But James'll be back tomorrow, I expect."

"Might be," said Tom, "Though I've never seen him do owt like that."

Josh was surprised to see a light on in the house as he came up the avenue. Inside a wan-looking Sheila was propped on the sofa in front of the fire.

"Discharged her early," said Dennis fussing round. After greeting her Josh headed into to the kitchen.

"Shall I make us my pasta?" he asked Dennis.

"Good idea - hadn't thought about food," was the harassed reply. After tea Josh broached the subject of 'Flames'.

"I tried the machine," he confessed. "James was ill."

"And...?" Dennis waited.

"It was good, I used the metallics."

"Right," said Dennis guardedly, "I'll have a look at it in the morning."

It was only later that Josh realised that he hadn't run a real tag in days. The following morning Josh did some shopping on his way to the works. Dennis was there before him.

"Ay up, here comes Picasso," said Tom. "I've shown him what you did, lad."

"And has he retired you?" ventured Josh.

"Not yet," said Tom and grinned. Josh grinned back.

"I'll take your sign round to Jack Ford and see if he thinks it'll do him," Dennis said. "Run up a few of your ideas for me. It's good to have something to show customers?" Josh stared but said nothing. Tom winked as the boy's glance brushed his face. Josh winked in reply.

The morning passed quickly. The Mac was a fantastic piece of kit and Josh was totally absorbed in what he was doing.

James returned to work on Wednesday. He found some of Josh's work in the computer memory.

"This 'Flames' is really good Josh," he said. 'You could draw out the actual letters a bit more with the enhancement programme - look, here, it helps to get rid of the shine..." The boy and the young man, heads together, discussed their ideas. Dennis nodded in their direction.

"Come on, Tom, we'll leave 'em to it."

After tea Josh left the house. "Back soon," he called. Dennis and Shelia looked at each other.

"Leave him," said Dennis. "Let him go, we'll see."

Josh shinned up the post at the edge of the embankment and edged his way across the iron bridge. Carefully taking a can from inside his parka he began to spray silver paint across the metal surface.

With two days left before school started Dennis and Josh travelled to work together. As they approached the railway yard Josh was noticeably quiet. Dennis found his eyes caught by a splash of colour high above the entrance. There in silver and purple on the iron bridge was the message, 'Gone legit - Be lucky,' signed with a familiar flourish. Nothing was said.

"Put the kettle on Tom," yelled Dennis. "Now lad, where's James? We need a new board for the Chinese restaurant - either of you any good at dragons?"

*Pat Almond*

# The Shepherd of the Hills

On long hot summer days you'll see him go
Armed with his crook, his collies ever near,
He'll be gathering his wandering flock
Of ewes and rams to dose and then to shear,
　　The weary shepherd of the hills.

In autumn he will once again be found
Striding the hills; to gather, his intent,
This time to separate the young from old,
When the healthy lambs to market will be sent
　　By the shepherd of the hills.

When storms pervade and snow is falling fast
And all around the blizzards rage and blow,
He boldly ventures forth, one thought in mind
To rescue ewes from banks of drifting snow,
　　The brave shepherd of the hills.

But when spring burgeons new amid the hills
And he surveys his growing flock with pride
He views the lively crop of lambs and smiles;
He cannot hide the pleasure deep inside,
　　The contented shepherd of the hills.

*Ann Bowes*

# An Angel of the North

## Nurse Maude Jagger S.R.N. S.C.M.  1914-2002

In 2002 we lost a very special person when Nurse Maude Jagger passed away.  She had been the keystone of Medical Care in the Esk Valley for 28 years and was loved and trusted by the whole community.  When I arrived to join Dr Peter Sowerby in 1977 she had already been retired for several years but as she was a patient of the practice we were in contact and it was always a pleasure to see her and to talk about the provision of healthcare to the community during her time.

Owing to her comprehensive local knowledge of the area, patients trusted her and would often confide in her.  In return she would 'keep an eye on the practice' and bring anything she thought was relevant to our notice.  She really was the practice 'Grandmother' and we all know how important they are.  Peter and I were delighted when she opened our new surgery at Egton in 1983.

Talking to her was always enjoyable and she was never short of a story to tell about her nursing days. Oh, how I wished I could have plugged her memory into a computer and down-loaded every event stored there.

One day when we were having a chat about some of her experiences, I said to her, "Could you write as much down as you can recall and then we will have a record of a very crucial working life?" She agreed and sometime later brought me a handwritten account, several pages long which was wonderful to read.  Below I have reproduced a word for word account of her life as written by Maude herself.  It is exactly Maude.

*'In 1946, with my husband Kenneth and my son David, I came to live in Glaisdale, the village where I was born. During that year I was asked to relieve the local midwife and delivered a baby in Houlsyke. My elder daughter, Margaret, was born in 1946 and the following year I was asked to apply for the District Nurse/Midwife post by the then Nursing Association. I was appointed to the post in August 1947 and so began 28 years of a very happy, interesting and varied career in this local area.*

The post also included Health Visiting and School Nursing, both new to me, but over the years I found them both rewarding and interesting.

There were three Doctors in this area at that time: Dr Armstrong was at Danby (I only worked with him when I relieved in that area), Dr Hyatt had a main surgery at Grosmont with 'Calling Houses' at Egton and Glaisdale but my main association was with Dr English, who had a main surgery at Sleights and branch surgeries at Goathland, Grosmont, Egton, Glaisdale and Lealholm. His workload was tremendous and he was loved by his patients and admired by his colleagues.

## Midwifery

The Antenatal care of women at that time was, to say the least, very haphazard. Some women did not book a Doctor because of the cost. Most women went to the Doctor and then asked the Midwife to call. I did not have any equipment to do any detailed antenatal work. I did not even possess a stethoscope or a sphygmomanometer or sticks to test urines. All I had was a Foetal Heart Stethoscope.

In 1948, after the advent of the National Health Service, things began to gradually improve. Dr Sowerby replaced Dr English on his retirement and when his new house at Egton was ready he opened a surgery there. I started an antenatal clinic there every Tuesday night. This was very helpful to me and I hope the patients found it was an advantage to them. The urines were tested regularly, blood specimens and blood pressures were taken and the results recorded on the patients' notes.

There was by now a Maternity Hospital at Eskdale, Whitby and quite a number of patients had their babies at that hospital but the antenatal care was still undertaken at Egton surgery. However some of the babies were still delivered at home. My own second daughter, Maureen, was born at home in 1949, delivered by the relief Midwife when Dr English was my Doctor. I had quite a few problems when delivering babies at home. One was the light. Some houses did not have electricity. I had to use a paraffin lamp, sometimes a stable lamp and sometimes an Aladdin lamp. The biggest problem was getting the lamp into the best position to cast light in the proper place so it did not cast a shadow. Also one had to be careful that the lamp did not get knocked over.

One house I went to did not have running water. I had to get water from a trough down the road then boil the water in a kettle over an open fire. Strangely enough we had few problems either with mothers or babies but some of these good results were due to the excellent help received from the patients' husbands, mothers and grandmothers.

Dr English did perform some forceps deliveries at home, usually asking another doctor to give the anaesthetic but he did perform one at Danby where he started with an open chloroform mask and I continued while he delivered the baby which was, sadly, stillborn. Previous to the opening of Eskdale hospital, the Caesarean sections were admitted to the Cottage Hospital at Whitby and delivered by the local doctors and Doctor English.

Prior to the advent of the National Health Service, the women paid me £1-10-0 which was paid to the Nursing Association. During my years on this District I delivered four sets of twins, some premature but all alive and well and I know all are still fit and well, both mentally and physically. One set of twin boys delivered on a farm were premature but when I visited them on the first morning, the father told me that the dog had licked them so they would be O.K. Not very professional but he was right. They progressed very well.

### General Nursing

When I first started on this district, I found District Nurses were not very popular. Some patients' relatives said, "Nurses made more work than the good they did. They made too much washing and needed too much running after." Over the years, with patience and I hope understanding their needs, I was accepted into their houses. Most of the very ill terminal cases were nursed at home. Heart conditions, strokes, cancers and gangrene of the feet etc. were all cared for by their relatives. A lot of the older people slept on feather beds and did not like any changes but these were not ideal for sick patients, especially if they were incontinent. Over the years people managed to buy divan beds which were easier but very low and sometimes we had to put them on wooden blocks to make things easier. I gradually managed to introduce draw sheets and draw mackintoshes which proved helpful but the biggest asset was the introduction of incontinence pads which were most acceptable.

Injections were few and far between at first but over the years penicillin injections became the order of the day. Going out in the early morning to give insulin injections to patients before breakfast was a regular part of General Nursing.

## Communications

My instructions for the nursing of patients were communicated to me by word of mouth rather than by letter. I used to visit Doctors' surgeries regularly, a practice not hitherto followed. I had a very good relationship with all the doctors and nurses in the area

## Transport

A bicycle would not have been a very sensible means of transport around this very hilly, scattered area. I couldn't ride one anyway so I had to learn to drive a car. I used to average 700-900 miles a month. In bad wintery weather I used all sorts of transport, including the train during the day, a tractor (someone else driving), a Land Rover, but sometimes I had to walk to maternity cases, very hard when I had to carry a bag and a large gas/air machine. I always managed to get to any call necessary, sometimes with my husband's help and also the patients' husbands who were always willing to come to my aid.

## Medication

Most medication at that time was in the form of medicines, not pills. The doctors did a lot of their own dispensing and carried medicines in their cars. I have known urgently needed medicines to be sent on a train and be collected at the station, either by me or the patient's relatives.

Doctor English had 'Miss Dickinson' as his dispenser and she came to Glaisdale on surgery days, Monday, Thursday and Saturday, to prepare the medicines and they were carried in a very big 'market basket'. When the cost of a prescription was one shilling, Doctor English would tell me not to collect a 'bob' from some households. "They won't have one," he said. I am afraid he was short of quite a few 'bobs' when he came to adding up his prescription charges.

## Health Visiting

This was a problem sometimes as all babies under five needed a visit at fairly regular intervals. In this scattered area this was not always easy and I sometimes spent two hours visiting one family in an outlying area. We did not have any play schools or nurseries so all had to be at home. I started a monthly 'Well baby clinic' in Lealholm and over the years this proved to be very popular and a great help to me. The M.O.H. visited to give immunisation injections etc and deal with any problems that arose. We did not have any special equipment for hearing or eye tests at that time so any defects had to be spotted by the parents' own observation or by me talking to the parents about a specific problem. Over the years equipment for testing eyes and ears did improve but with the help of the GPs and the MOH I hope we did not miss any serious defects that these under fives had. I visited the elderly fairly frequently reporting on their needs including Doctor's visits.

## School Nursing

I was the 'Nitty Nurse' responsible for schools at Glaisdale, Egton, Egton Bridge and Lealholm and when relieving a colleague at Grosmont and Fryup. On the whole most children were very clean but occasionally we had some head infestation but with treatment and co-operation with the families this was usually cleared up very quickly. Ringworm was not uncommon and impetigo at times was a problem but with co-operation with the parents, who all visited the Doctors, they were kept under control.

The Medical Officers also visited the schools at regular intervals which I also attended. I had the advantage of knowing most of the children before their school days, and knowing their medical histories and their home background was, I hope, a help to parents, their children and the MOH.

To sum up, my 28 years spent in this area were the most interesting, rewarding and educational part of my 40 years nursing. The patients I cared for were wonderful people, responsive, patient, long suffering and always grateful. With the unfailing help from the relatives and good medical care from the doctors, I was able to nurse these people through their illnesses, either to better health or the end of their lives. The work was hard and sometimes very demanding. The hours were long especially as I had quite a few night calls from midwifery and sometimes general cases. The off- duty was 24 hours per week, one weekend per month and three weeks' holiday a year, eventually six weeks.

The day I retired I received some wonderful gifts from all these grateful people but I could not have managed any of it without the help of my husband, my children, the domestic *helps, the doctors, my nursing colleagues and all the staff at Egton surgery which I still attend as a patient and, I am glad to say, as a colleague and, I hope, a friend.'*

*Photo supplied*

My colleague Doctor Peter Sowerby worked very closely with Maude over many years and, as such, can give us his first hand knowledge of working with Maude.

**Tribute to Maude**
**Dr. Peter Sowerby**

*'Maude was an extraordinary woman and an exceptional member of her profession. She was one of the last of the great tradition of nurses in remote places, who were all thing to all men. She was Nurse, Midwife, Health Visitor, all three in one person, day in and day out.*

*She loved every minute of her job. She carried it lightly too, almost belying the strict professional standards from which she never deviated. She was nothing if not totally accessible. She was a gentle, warm and sensitive person with a sense of humour to match any situation. This immediately put everyone at ease, however frightened or distressed, enabling her to use her quite astonishing professional skill or knowledge, whatever she encountered. She was never at a loss. She was also quite exceptionally observant, learning quickly from her experience, and able to pass it on to others in a way that few nurses are able.*

*But midwifery was her passion and she was, without doubt, the finest midwife I have ever met. I have no idea how many babies she delivered but it must be a thousand or more. My profession trusted Maude as few nurses have ever been trusted. All folk who lived in this Vale knew it, but they also knew that she would never hesitate to call a doctor if necessary. More than that, Maude did an immeasurable amount of good. Her warmth, her compassion and her intelligent humanity brought hope and comfort to the lives of all who needed her, while her skill and knowledge saved countless lives and limbs. She will be remembered for many generations to come with love and thanks for a very selfless life."*

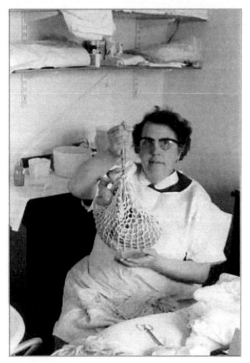

There is little I can add to all this other than to say that Maude, Peter and I were all very privileged to provide healthcare to the people of the Esk Valley and continue something started by Maude. She really was 'An Angel of the North'.

*Alan Brighouse*

Maude weighing
a new-born baby
*Photo supplied*

# Cow's Calvin'

My introduction to North Yorkshire, and the Esk Valley in particular, began in 1973 when we purchased a holiday home near Houlsyke. We then spent many happy times in the area which we found to be one of the friendliest places we had visited and a sharp contrast to my life in Kirkella, West Hull. I had been in practice there, a typical suburban practice, since 1962.

In 1977, Dr Peter Sowerby, who until that time had been single-handed, asked me to join him as a partner. So began the happiest time of my working life until I retired from the NHS in 1994. The two practices could not have been more different but I was slightly surprised when Peter told me it would take five years to really get to know the practice and the area. But he was right and it was a treasure yet to come.

When I first joined Peter, I had, for while, to commute at the weekends to my home in Kirkella. One weekend, as I left the Egton surgery on a Friday afternoon, a late visit came in. A farmer had come in from the fields with a severe headache which sounded serious, so I told Peter I would call and see him on my way home to Kirkella. When I got to the farm, it did indeed look serious and could possibly have been a brain haemorrhage which would require urgent admission to Middlesbrough Hospital. I called Peter on our practice radio and he told me he would organise the admission, so I went on my way to Kirkella.

As, on that Friday afternoon, I had been unable to get to the bank in Kirkella, on the Monday morning I was fortunately able to cash a cheque at the Midland Bank bus in Glaisdale. There was a group of farmers ahead of me and of course I had not been in the area long enough for them to recognise me. I soon realised they were talking about the Friday patient and in no time I knew... yes, he had been admitted to Middlesbrough; which ward he was on; that it was a possible brain haemorrhage; who was taking his wife to visit him; who was organising his milking and that the outlook was good! I soon realised that this was a very different world to the one I had left and it made me feel very happy that I had decided to come to the Egton Practice.

Already having a holiday home in the area was a great help in getting to know the practice, the patients and their families. However it was their attitude to life that was so endearing and in time I came to realise what it was that made them so. As a farming community, two things were apparent. Firstly, their lives were very much dictated by the elements and secondly, they were used to seeing animals born, live and die. It was the natural way of living and it gave them a very philosophical attitude to life. This had a distinct influence on their medical care and always had to be taken into account.

I often discussed this with Nurse Maude Jagger, our retired District Nurse and a fount of knowledge in nursing matters. She told me lots of stories about her twenty-eight years as District Nurse in the area and one of many comes to mind. She was in the process of delivering a mother at a farm where there was no electricity and she had to resort to using a paraffin lamp as a source of light. Suddenly the husband came into the bedroom and proceeded to pick up the lamp and head for the door.

"Where are you going with that?" she cried.

"Cow's calvin' and I need it in t'barn," and off he went, leaving Maude to sort everything out, which she did and all was well. Cow's calvin' is a number one priority on farms in the Esk Valley!

Many years later, I was called to see a farmer who was obviously having a heart attack and I advised his admission to Whitby Hospital for care. However there was no way he would agree to being hospitalised. He was determined to stay on his farm, so I compromised and had a bed brought downstairs to give him easier toilet access and I insisted on strict bed rest. The next day, I was on my house visits and driving past the farm which was adjacent to the roadside. There was the farmer, on a cold day, dressed in pyjamas, dressing gown and slippers, peering into an outbuilding. I was furious and I screeched to a halt and strode towards him to vent my anger for disobeying my orders. When I started to express my fury, he just turned to me and said quietly, "Cow's calvin', tha can't stop i' bed when t'cow's calvin'." It was said in such a calm, straight manner that I soon realised that no amount of reprimanding from me would alter the situation, so I got back in the car and drove off, quietly smiling to myself and thinking of Maude. He, of course, fully recovered and went on to live a full life for many years!

Along with Peter Sowerby and Maude Jagger, I have some wonderful memories of our time providing medical care for the patients of the Esk Valley, some happy, some humorous and some painfully sad but, throughout it all, we had the unswerving loyalty of our patients, their instant offers of help in difficult times and their wonderful attitude to life. What a lucky man I have been to live and work in such a place!

*Alan Brighouse*

## Botham's Lady

Pies and pastries, bread and cakes are her stock in trade,
Serving at the counter where the bakery goods are made.
Her customers are hungry for the smiles she gives for free,
"Can I help you love? I'll pack it, pass your bag up here to me."
A wispy strand escapes her cap, her buttons under strain,
There is sadness in the gentle eyes although she smiles again.
A mother to her customers, a mother with no child;
A mother with a mother who will not be denied.
She hurries home on aching feet to reassure and feed
Her parent, who is now her child, demanding in her need.
Like the pensioners and teenagers she serves with care and grace
She tends the aged despot with the pinched and wrinkled face
With smiles. Soft-voiced and patient, she does what must be done.
Then downstairs to the sitting room to claim the time she`s won.
She rests. A quiet moment in another hectic day.
A cup of tea, a magazine, an urge to walk away
Is in her heart, by conscience stilled; she has no chance to seek
The dark-haired handsome stranger who would kiss her floury cheek,
Or a man plain-faced but strong with love, to work with her and share
A swaddled child with curled pink hands and a drift of silken hair.
She sighs and takes her dirty mug. Will her day ever come?
Or will she stay behind the counter - everybody's Mum?

*Pat Almond*

# Seasonings

## Winter

Your cold, damp fingers creep upon us
    As autumn draws to an end,
And when it's least expected
    Those icy tentacles you send
To freeze like rock the sodden earth
    And crystallize the grass,
You chill the air we all must breathe
    And gild each pool with glass.
You delight in shortening our daylight hours,
    Enjoy each long dark night,
And just for one more extra pleasure
    You'll clothe the world in white.

But even you can't stay forever,
    You strength will lose its hold,
Your grip will weaken and you'll grow tired
    And the air will feel less cold,
Your freezing power will last no more,
    You'll struggle with the sun,
And as we see each day grow longer
    You'll find life's not much fun.
You'll disappear for another year
    Admitting your defeat,
And when spring breaks to take your place
    Your end will be complete.

*Ann Bowes*

# Grasp the Nettle!

Grasp the nettle, seize the day,
Smell the warmth of new mown hay,
Embrace the challenge, face each storm,
It's yours to take, don't get forlorn.
Love the journey through your life,
Happiness amongst the strife
And, if it in your nature be,
Grasp the nettle and be free.

*Julia Organ*

# Spring Sonnet

A spring of lightness and brightness, arrayed
With primrose, daffodil and deep, green grass.
The days are long and loud with birdsong. Pass
Slowly, though actively, as nests are made.
Green shoots develop, embrangle, invade,
Undergrowth flourishes, insects amass,
Become fly-through protein for birds that pass
On their day-long nursery feeding raid.

But all is not idyllic at this time,
From up the chimney with a skirring hum,
Two hundred grams of soot-disturbing bird
Announces his presence with sooty grime.
A fire can't be lit till autumn's come
As this nesting bird will not be deterred.

*Kate Trewren*

# An Autumn Treat

The fallen plums adorn the lawn
And flies and wasps adorn the plums,
The branches laden, hanging low
Amidst the sound of insect hums.
Across the lawn with practised ease
A hedgehog ventures to the trees.
She moves with grace, at steady pace,
Towards the purple plums.
Her long legs pause, as, snout stretching out,
She snuffles, forages and feeds.
Feasting for winter, long-term needs.
The flies attack her prickly back
But well-developed ears reprise limitations of small eyes,
She merely twitches and gorges on
Ignoring the dive-bombing flies.

*Kate Trewren*

*Illustration - H Walker*

# Sweet and Sour

## Letters in Stone

Blood oozed from under a dirt-encrusted nail then congregated on his finger tip before slowly dripping to the stony earth at Charlie Groves's feet. This discovery was accompanied by a low groan and then in an attempt to ease the pain in his damaged digit he stuffed the whole of his hand into his armpit.

Charlie had been working this stretch of wall for the past seven days. It had been in poor condition and the new owners of Castle Bray had employed him to rebuild a lot of the walls around the outlying fields.

It was a cold spring morning on the moor. An icy sea breeze, held low by the stratus clouds above, crept through clothes and fleeces alike. A small flock of Scottish Blackface sheep stood with their backs into the wind and watched intently at Charlie's antics as he paced around in small circles until the pain and blood loss subsided. With his eyes screwed up against the dull throbbing pain he sat down on the lee side of the wall, protected from the elements.

It had been a morning with few attributes.

Castle Bray was a grand name for a not unsubstantial farm set in the almost hidden valley of Crook Beck, high on the exposed North York Moors.

Charlie loved his work, by and large, but today seemed not to be going so well. The hammer blows which were normally controlled and precise, shaping the random stones, had become haphazard and consequently hazardous. This was the cause of Charlie's discomfort.

Binding his finger with a plaster from what he laughingly called his First Aid kit (a clean hanky, plasters and some headache pills), Charlie waited with fingers raised. As the throbbing pain slowly passed he rummaged in his bag to reveal a thermos flask. On opening it the aroma of fresh ground coffee wafted across his nose. He drank in its heady scent and settled down to an early lunch. Perhaps the afternoon would bring more success.

Charlie sat, his back resting against the wall, his pain almost forgotten. Warm coffee raised his core temperature and he munched through crispy lettuce, tomato and boiled bacon sandwiches held in blood and dirt-encrusted hands. Things were perhaps not so bad.

As he sat, the clouds slowly parted and sun bathed the area with its warm golden rays.

Charlie's half cup of coffee was cold when he awoke from his unplanned slumber and as he gently rubbed his sleep-laden eyes he realised an hour had passed and the afternoon was upon him.

The afternoon did, in fact, improve. Soon Charlie had to remove his coat and shirt as the air temperature began to rise. Rivulets of perspiration coursed down his dusty body as he worked tirelessly, only pausing to check on his handiwork. The rebuilt section of the wall stood resplendent in the afternoon sun and sparkled as mica facets reflected the clear rays of light.

*Photo supplied*

Working past his normal finishing time the lone worker recouped the morning's loss and more.

The next section was a heavily-built corner. Charlie started to dismantle the damaged section and working methodically he removed the capstones, setting them down on the soft moorland turf. He was removing the third layer when something caught his eye. A scrap of yellowed paper appeared, wedged between the large sandstone blocks. Charlie's inquisitive nature made him stop his work and carefully retrieve the fragment of what appeared to be a letter.

When the paper was carefully unfolded it revealed one line of immaculate copper-plate handwriting and one line of slightly less legible script written by a different hand.  It read, 'I will be walking Spot on Sunday around 2.00 o'clock, with luck we may meet', and was signed CW  Beneath this came the reply, ponderously written in pencil, 'I will be here early, I can't wait, CS.'

Charlie carefully placed the paper in his empty food box and wondered who CW and CS were as he continued his work.

It wasn't long before Charlie discovered several more notes, some with more in-depth information.  In one such note CW explained that her Daddy disapproved of their meetings.  In another, CS told how he had been to see Mr Kitchener's men and suggested they should meet soon as he might have to go away.

As the light faded, work stopped for the night.  The waller collected the notes together and with reverence he carried his little bundle of intrigue home.

Early the next morning, with the sun barely over the horizon, Charlie commenced work on the wall.  The slips of paper he had previously found told a story of an early 1900's love affair, shared happiness, life in the Dales, farming and of a young man's ambition to join the war effort.

Charlie removed more layers and was pleased to find more brown-edged slips of paper which again he collected.  After reading each one he placed them in what he thought was a chronological order and discovered that CS did in fact join Kitchener's army.

The corner was almost dismantled before Charlie found another scrap of paper.  This time the copper-plate written question was answered by an equally well written reply.  Charlie was taken aback by this new revelation; he felt let down and confused.  He stared at the second line of script.  There were no initials.  Could it be that CW had found a new suitor? Around him came the far off call of the curlew, a haunting sound that today seemed like a call of desolation.

Charlie examined the remainder of the wall looking for the slip of paper that may contain the answer. He frantically removed the remaining stones without success.

Charlie was caught up in a living story book, but a book without an ending.

From this vantage point Castle Bray came into view, framed between a large Mountain Ash tree and the wall.  The grey buildings stood out starkly against the backdrop of golden brown bracken that graced the valley's steep sides.

Charlie stood almost dejected. So near but so far, he thought. Then his eyes alighted on the silver bark of the Rowan tree. There, carved in the living tissues of its trunk, were the letters CW and CS enclosed in a heart. Strangely though, the arrow, which is normally shown piercing the heart, was set below, pointing to the craggy face of the wall. Charlie peered to where the arrow pointed. There in a tight joint between two stones protruded the blackened edge of a sliver of paper. Carefully, with trembling fingers, Charlie withdrew the folded sheet and realised that in this message there had been a role reversal. The note read, 'Will you marry me? CS' and in the best copper-plate script came the simple reply, 'Yes, CW'.

Charles and Charlotte Stone (nee Webster) took over the Webster family farm of Castle Bray in 1924, raising four children, Charles, Roger, Charlotte and Elizabeth. They finally passed away within two weeks of each other in the year 1978.

*Paul Wedgwood*

*Photo: P Wedgwood*

# Coming Home

Glancing up at the office clock Kate wearily pushed her hair away from tired eyes. Already it was 9.30 and almost completely dark outside. A lot more reading was needed and notes had to be typed if she was to be ready for tomorrow's court case. She found her mobile phone and almost without looking pressed her home number. While awaiting a reply, she poured herself a welcome glass of water - why was it taking Thomas so long to answer?

"At last! Where were you?" she curtly enquired.

"Watching TV."

"I'm at the office as you'll have gathered and still not finished and I'm too weary to drive home tonight so I'll bunk down at the flat and see you tomorrow evening. I need to be here for the opening of the trial anyway so it's silly to drive a couple of hours home just to have five hours sleep and then rush back to Leeds. Okay?"

"Yep, Okay." Thomas's phone went dead.

"Oh... and good night to you, too!" Kate snapped.

It was almost an hour later when the phone on her desk buzzed. A man's voice asked, "You still there?" It was Alex, a partner in the firm. "I tried your flat and your home number but as there was no reply guessed you were still working. Do you want the good news?"

"Of course."

"Just heard the case has been adjourned for a couple of weeks, new evidence or something... So... go home, night-night."

Kate put the phone down, grabbed her jacket, plus bag and car keys, turned off the computer and lights and locked the office. She'd get home after all and perhaps needn't even make the journey back tomorrow. A whole weekend to relax. Guess Thomas will be pleased. Her brow wrinkled as she puzzled over why he hadn't answered the phone when Alex called.

It was well past midnight as Kate quietly parked the car. There were no lights on in the house but the porch automatically illuminated as she opened the outer door and attempted to unlock the main door. The key jammed.

"Damn, damn, damn!" Now she'd have to creep round the garden and knock on their bedroom window. Thank goodness they lived in a single storey house. Thomas might be miffed, but heck, did she do this sort of thing often? Nope! She removed her high heels, peeled off her tights then gingerly tiptoed up the path. She was almost there, then calamity, she banged her toe and let out a yell. Well, now there was no need to knock on anything after that racket! The window was flung open, Thomas peered out, then, abruptly slammed the window shut again. Kate hobbled through the flowerbed and hammered on the glass with her fist, shouting, "Thomas open the door... or at least open the window!" The window opened again and Thomas's anguished face peered out.

"What the hell are you doing home?"

"Well, what the hell are you doing? Thomas, unlock the door at once... now!"

Kate limped back to the front door and waited but nothing happened. She pushed open the letter-box and peered into a dark empty hall. Listening, she could hear the murmur of voices, and was sure one sounded like a woman's, but she couldn't be sure and still nobody appeared. Kate's rage erupted, her toe hurt like mad, she was tired and now this!

"If there's a woman with you," she screamed, "you get the tart out of my bed, out of my room, out of my house... do you hear me Thomas... Thomas, do you hear me!"

Kate was breathing hard and trembling with both shock and fury. Still no activity came from within the house, no lights, nothing. She had to do something but what? Think, think, she told herself.

She walked down the path again via the woodshed and sat down on a large upturned log, feeling sick. How dare Thomas be unfaithful! Suddenly a blind rage swamped her and looking round she saw a long-handled axe. Grabbing hold of the shaft she made her way back to the door. Swinging the axe above her head she slammed it into the woodwork, splintering the horrible dark brown door. The noise was horrendous but she didn't give a damn. She raised the axe again, almost falling backwards with the exertion, but, before she could strike, the door slowly opened. Dropping the axe, Kate forced her way inside and saw Thomas standing in the milky moonlight and behind him someone else. Switching the light on, Kate gave a strangled gasp as she saw her close friend Jill's terrified face turn ashen-white. Thomas looked idiotic, his mouth opening and shutting like a demented goldfish. "It's all your fault," he began.

"My fault! How have you conjured that one up?" Kate turned on Jill. "Some friend... you prissy miss prim... why, Jill? Why? What have I ever done to hurt you?"

"Leave her alone. Blame me if you must." Thomas was beginning to assert himself.

"Leave her alone... that whore! I'll kill her." Kate ran towards the kitchen, wrenched open a drawer and grabbing a large steel knife returned, her outrage boiling over again.

"Oh, hell hath no fury like a woman scorned," scoffed Thomas, looking defiant, until he saw the knife.

"Kate, don't be stupid... have some control... we'll talk." He pushed Jill through an opening and following, slammed the door shut, putting his weight against it. At that second the knife blade hit the door becoming firmly embedded in the wood. Kate heaved to pull it out but thankfully for Thomas's sake it wouldn't budge. She heard Thomas calling the police and almost regrettably decided she should leave. She got into her car and drove down the lane but then stopped and backed into a copse of trees that overlooked her home. She switched off the lights and engine... waiting. Sure enough, along came two police cars, blue lamps flashing and sirens making one hell of a noise as they raced past her hiding place. Kate so wished she was a fly on the wall at home, seeing and hearing everything. Well, what would her disturbed neighbours make of it all? They were in for a treat. She felt as though she was on a 'high'. Uncontrollable giggles intermingled with sobs as she drove off into the night.

Thankful to have the apartment to return to in Leeds, Kate nursed her heartache. Work was her solace in this time of recovery. She knew sooner or later she would have to see Thomas, but for many weeks she couldn't bring herself to meet him face to face. Eventually, after frequent in-depth talks on the phone, she said she'd go home... after all, it was her home too.

There were faults on both sides; they both accepted it! Thomas hated Kate being away all week and when home she was always on the phone to Alex, raising the suspicion that he was more than a colleague in the office.

"Thomas!" Kate took his hands, "Alex is work... nothing but work. I love my job, always have... we like the income. You have been able to retire early and I thought life was good. Where did it all go wrong?"

'Still', thought Kate, 'at least I have a new front door... how I hated that old dark wooden one!'

*Pat Henderson*

# Our Love was like a Shining Star

Our love was like a shining star
Lost in a golden hue,
A love we knew could never be
Yet constantly it grew.

A fleeting glance across a room,
A twinkle in your eye
Could set my pulses racing fast,
My spirits flying high.

And if by chance your presence was
So close that I could feel
Your warm breath soft upon my face,
My senses then would reel.

And if your hand should gently brush
So lightly on my skin,
I'd feel excited tremors stir
Hot passions deep within.

It was a love that never dimmed,
A love forever true,
For you became a part of me
And I, a part of you.

We shared a special kind of love
And like that shining star,
It never lost its golden power
That bound us from afar.

*Inspired by Robbie Burns -   'My love is like a red, red rose'*

*Ann Bowes*

# Walking on Sunshine

How can anyone walk on sunshine? Dr Who maybe, or some yogi – but for Sadie those days out were all sunshine, just like the song, and her aches and pains seemed to melt away. Her wedge-shaped, mobile Zimmer frame was more of an encumbrance than a help. Besides, it inhibited her sense of style.

Let me set the scene for you: meet Sarah Elizabeth Quinlan who's lived for 82 summers, this one destined to be her last. She's a lovely lady who is on a day trip to Whitby with her carer, Evadne. Sadie is wearing a classy trench-coat, open, over a beige skirt and a pink top. She wears a white hat adorned with a pink rose and has sensible sandals on her feet. Large sunglasses add an aura of mystery and a "bamboo pink" lipstick makes her feel young. (Only really old ladies wear red!)

Sadie has spent the last three years living in a care-home on the outskirts of Middlesbrough. She hates it (the care-home, not Middlesbrough, though perhaps she hates that too). She doesn't really need a carer but Margaret's idea of giving her a day out is to send her on these trips. Evadne uses one of Margaret's cars and is paid by the hour – minimum wage, cash in hand. Margaret is much too busy to take her own mother out.

Now I'd better introduce you to Evadne Trasp. As it's a warm day she is wearing a tee-shirt and shorts, not really flattering attire. Evadne is in her early thirties and is a single mum of two. She has ambition, intelligence and compassion. She and Sadie make an odd couple, Sadie being tall and thin whilst Evadne is short and dumpy, but they thoroughly enjoy their days out together. This is why Evadne is prepared to work for less than she is paid for her care-home shifts. I think the scene has been set and now it's time to focus on that sunny day in Whitby.

It was a Friday, so I was working on the till when Sadie and Evadne entered the shop.

"I'll just put this here for a while as I don't really need it," announced Sadie, kindly depositing her walking-aid with me. I gratefully smiled and watched as she gravitated towards the handbags and Evadne headed for the tops. The shop wasn't busy so I was able to observe Sadie as she picked up and inspected each bag, smiling happily and humming to herself.

Evadne came to the till to purchase a white tee-shirt for £2.99 (not dissimilar to the one she was wearing) and then went to show it to Sadie.

"I'll leave you to browse for a while," she said, "I'll just be outside enjoying the sunshine."

After a little while, Sadie approached the till. The shop had become quite busy but Evadne had not yet returned. Sadie was bestrewn with handbags and shopping bags, variously coloured but decidedly not tat. I started ringing the items through and found that one of the bags had about ten items of jewellery inside – meanwhile Sadie had seen two other bags, hanging near the till that she wanted.

"They'll tell me off for spending all my money!" she said with a gleeful smile.

Question: Should one take money from an old lady for items she cannot possibly need but, at that moment in time, definitely wants? Further Question: Can she afford all this?

Of course I didn't voice these questions and Sadie soon clarified her financial situation by taking a little drawstring purse from her pocket and removing a roll of notes. I was so relieved to see Evadne return!

"My, what a lot you've found!" she commented but didn't seem perturbed.

"She loves shopping," she added quietly. "And she ends up giving most of it away."

The bill came to £31.29. Sadie paid £30.00 whilst Evadne provided £1.29, so that Sadie could keep her remaining £5 note for later. Sadie retrieved her walking aid, quite useful to hang her bag of bags from, and they headed out of the store. Within two minutes Sadie was back; she had found a silky sequinned belt.

"It's just so pretty, I couldn't resist it," she explained.

"Yes, it's lovely," I agreed, taking her last five pounds from her.

And that should have been that. I'd had a salutary glimpse into what could be my future and vowed to curtail my impulse-buying. However, towards the end of the year I spotted a picture of Sadie in the daily paper. In fact there were three pictures: one of a rather younger looking Sadie, one of a rather smarter-looking Evadne and one of a rather cross-looking Margaret Montgomery.

## LOTTERY WINNER LEAVES FORTUNE TO CARER

Mrs Sarah Quinlan, 82, who won £7.2 million on the National Lottery in 2006 and who died earlier this year, has astounded her family by leaving the bulk of her £5 million estate to her carer, Ms Evadne Trasp.

"We shall certainly contest the will," said her daughter, Margaret Montgomery. Ms Montgomery, the owner of 'Whorls and Curls' – the New Romantic hair-care fashion venture on Teesside (established 2006), stressed how upset and betrayed the family had felt at the terms of her mother's will.

"I had no idea that Sadie was rich," said Evadne Trasp, post-graduate student at the University of Teesside. "She was such a happy, carefree spirit and I miss her."

I put down the newspaper and gazed at nothing – she'd been rich and I had felt guilty at taking her money. I thought of Sadie and all her purchases, of her delight in them. Evadne had given her space and freedom to do things her way, showing her the respect that her domineering daughter obviously hadn't. I remembered the sunshine of that day – and I shall always remember Sadie.

*Kate Trewren*

# Grace

Grace is the most amazing person I have ever known. She glows with a light which is love and happiness rolled into one and she shines with an inner peace, a beacon in the darkness. Amazing Grace.

Her voice carried down the breeze to the place where I was working, mending a fence that ran down to the wood. How sweet the sound of that voice as it fell softly around the anemones and daffodils that grew in profusion around me!

It was that voice that came to me when I lay in a coma caused by drink and drugs. A voice that came through a haze of intoxication. I was a wasted man, far along the road of self destruction.

Why did this female want to spend time with me? I led an existence far from the normal: stealing, lying and cheating my way through life.

But things for me began to change. 'I once was lost but now I am found'. Grace showed me a way out of my life style, an avenue that led me away from that endless road that would eventually lead to death. But I at first couldn't see it; I had become blind to the things that were wrong in my life. Grace showed me the way, the truth and the light. I 'was blind but now I see'.

Perhaps it was that voice of hers, angelic, creative, loving and compassionate, that led me away from self-destruction. Grace showed me places I had only seen in my childhood dreams. She took me out of the concrete jungle, away from torment, away from my self-induced confinement. She took me to hills and dales, wooded glades and sparkling waterfalls, to blue skies and sunshine not tainted by industrial pollution and obscured by office blocks and high-rise flats. She led me into a quiet, tranquil land where my soul could breathe.

Amazing Grace showed me a life that I could embrace.

It was not easy to kick the drugs and alcohol habit. Life was full of dangers as I suffered withdrawal symptoms and the infamous DT's. But cocooned in love and compassion I eventually emerged a new man. 'Through many dangers, toils and snares I have already come. Tis' grace that brought me safe this far. And grace will lead me home.' Home to a life that I could never have envisaged, a home that is full of sunshine, laughter, happiness and love.

One evening, as the sun was setting and long beams of golden light flooded through the diamond panes of the mullioned windows, I gazed transfixed into the eyes of Grace, amazing Grace, as she explained the truth behind my miraculous change, my transformation from a caterpillar, chomping on the leaves of life, to the butterfly, with wings of freedom.

She told me of a man born over two thousand years ago whose life had changed the world of my amazing Grace. As we sat near the brazier, cosseted in the warmth of the glowing embers, I believed all she told me because I knew in my heart, which was once made of stone, it was right. I knew her words were the truth. She told me, 'The Lord has promised good for me' and 'His word my hope was secure' and suddenly I knew whatever would happen in my life he would look after me, 'He will my shield and portion be, as long as life endures'.

Our life together has spanned many years, and her voice still sounds sweet in my ears. The same voice that called me out of the darkness so long ago, now calls an old man in for his supper.

As I walk, I hear my own singing voice echoing around the farm buildings and there across the yard Grace's beautiful smiling face, framed in the kitchen window, looks out. And I notice her mouth is singing the same words as I am. "Yes, when this heart and flesh shall fail, and mortal life shall cease, I shall possess within the veil, a life of joy and peace."

*Paul Wedgwood*

# Game Pie

## The Point-to-Point

The day had come and everywhere
　　Excitement seemed to fill the air,
　　　　Enthusiasts from near and far
　　　　　　Came flocking in, car after car.

Mingling crowds could now be heard
　　This Saturday of March the third,
　　　　Shouting bookies tell their odds
　　　　　　With many a wink and oft a nod.

At paddock rail where lookers on
　　Can study form for right or wrong,
　　　　Fit horses being led around
　　　　　　Churning up the heavy ground.

With glistening coat and head held high
　　A flighty beast shows white of eye.
　　　　Jockeys mount, then to the start,
　　　　　　A sight to gladden any heart.

They're off, I see the flag go up,
　　Each trying hard to win the cup,
　　　　Galloping hooves fly over brush,
　　　　　　The crowd goes into silent hush.

The last time round excitement mounts,
　　Each second to these horses counts,
　　　　Last fence in sight, the crowd all cheer
　　　　　　Amid the strain and sweat and fear.

The race is won - they all come in,
　　The bookies pay out on the win.
　　　　It is a day enjoyed by most,
　　　　　　The local point-to-point will boast.

*Julia Organ*

# Twelfth Man

Simon stared out of the changing room window, a worried look on his face. On that warm, sunny afternoon he watched the umpires march towards the centre and place the stumps in position. Stalwarts of the game and numerous supporters were filling the spectators' seats. The young lad trembled at the thought of walking out there to bat. The tall athletic frame of his brother, Marty, was standing near the wicket with the opposing captain. Marty flipped a coin in the air and stooped to retrieve it before shaking hands with the broad-shouldered red-haired youth. Simon sighed. If only Mark wasn't on holiday and Derek hadn't broken his thumb. And yesterday another member of the team had gone down with a virus. He recalled the conversation he'd had with Marty.

"You know I'm useless at cricket."

"You probably won't have to play," Marty reassured him. "I'm sure Pete will have recovered in time for the match." It was the semi-final of the Cup.

"But I haven't any whites."

"There'll be an old pair that I've grown out of – they'll fit you fine," Marty coaxed.

"What about boots?"

"Wear your white trainers."

"Why do I have to wear whites if I'm only twelfth man?"

"It looks better, more professional." Marty smiled at his young brother in encouragement. Simon was well aware of his cricketing shortcomings and hoped he'd not be needed. But now, much to Simon's dismay, Peter hadn't recovered and he had to play.

"Come on, Simon, hurry up and get changed," encouraged Vernon, a big burly lad who opened the batting. He was practising imaginary strokes with his trusty Kookaburra. "Don't look so worried; you're in at number 11 so you probably won't have to bat."

"I hope not. You know I'm rubbish."

"You'll be fine. Just a bit of fielding to do," he grinned. Marty entered the dressing-room.

"Pads on Verne. I lost the toss and we're batting."

Simon changed and went outside to sit with the others players. Soon the twang of bat on leather brought loud applause as big Vernon hit form, sending boundary shots in all directions. How Simon admired him!  The opening bowlers were fast and fairly accurate so a huge six over the pavilion was much applauded.  A mighty cheer from the fielders erupted as the first wicket fell.  This was followed a few overs later by two more dismissals.  Next in was Marty who strode out with an air of confidence and took up his position at the crease.  He and Vernon soon took the score to 85 but then disaster struck.  Big Verne was adjudged out lbw.  He walked off somewhat aggrieved as the umpire raised the dreaded finger.  The score ticked along slowly and more wickets fell.  Marty was eventually caught at slip and, as he came off, Simon suddenly realised eight wickets were down.

"Hurry Simon; get padded up, it's you next," urged his brother.  As Simon strapped on his pads he prayed the overs would run out before a wicket fell.  It was not to be.  He heard the fielders cheer as an appeal for a run out was given.  Simon made his self-conscious way to the middle.  The outgoing batsman encouraged the young lad as they met.

"Do your best, Simon, try and let Bobby keep the strike."  Simon gave a weak smile in contrast to his inner feelings.  How could anyone enjoy this?  He felt terrified as he took up his position, thankful that he wasn't facing.  The bowler thundered in but the other batsman managed a fine edge and called for a run.  Simon ran as fast as he could.  He turned and realised his team-mate was trying for two.  Simon raced back and amazingly reached his ground.  The next ball was pushed to gully and they ran a quick single, leaving Simon to face the bowling.  Two balls remained.  He took guard but the ball flew past him before he'd raised his bat, just missing the off stump.  Taking a deep breath he braced himself for the final ball.  Alas, it sent his middle stump flying from the ground.  No miracle today.

"Come on lads, let's go."  Marty led his team out after the interval and positioned them, sending Simon out to the far boundary.

"Get behind the ball and throw it in as hard as you can," he smiled.  The opposition's target was 136 runs.

Simon watched in admiration as the opening batsmen stroked the ball around the field, soon reaching 50.  Marty changed tactics and brought on his spin bowler.  The batsman edged a catch behind and the next player was soon making his way back to the pavilion, having been clean-bowled.  One of the new batsmen was the big red-headed captain.  He cautiously defended the first couple of balls but soon got the spinner's measure and began hitting fours in all directions.  They reached 100 and although wickets were falling, the redhead was still there, pushing the score on. Simon managed to field some balls but was unable to prevent several others from crossing the line. Marty kept moving his fielders around, encouraging them as he did so.

"Come on lads, let's close in now. Stop the singles." The situation was tense. Two overs remained with the opposition needing 28 runs to win. Trying to keep strike, redhead went for boundaries and hit three off the penultimate over, leaving 16 runs required from the last six balls. Marty brought back his spinner. The first ball flew Simon's way. He raced towards it, diving to the ground, but in vain; it crossed the line. The next two balls beat the bat, bringing loud encouragement for the bowler. The fourth hit the pad, resulting in two leg-byes. Two balls remained as redhead squared up to the next delivery. He edged it past the wicketkeeper, beating first slip and it raced away for four. Tension was high. A six off the final ball would mean defeat. A mighty swing connected, lofting the ball high into the air. Everyone watched, convinced it was the winning runs. Simon stared too, open-mouthed, as it sailed high above him. Suddenly he realised he was right underneath the descending ball. He cupped his hands as it thudded into his chest, sending him to the ground. Shouts and cheers rang in his ears as he lay there on the grass, gasping for breath, still clutching the ball firmly in his grasp. He was aware of Marty pulling him to his feet as the players gathered round.

"Well done, Simon." Others joined in. "Brilliant catch. We've won, we've won."

"We have?" croaked Simon. Marty threw an arm round his young brother.

"Yes, we're in the final," he exclaimed. Simon shook his head.

"No, *you* are in the final."

*Ann Bowes*

# A Beater's Lament

Unseen within green spongy reeds,
With watchful bright and beady eye,
Sit tight, pretty pheasant, indeed,
Sit tight in your heather, don't fly!
Danger ahead, as the cool moorland breeze
Sends sure, soft scent through wind-bent trees.
Sit tight, pretty pheasant, sit tight.

Crunch of brown bracken and dogs panting by,
Desperate to nudge you to flight and to die.
You'd fidget and fuss and would clumsily fly,
Your hold on sweet life seems flimsy and slight.
I'm cheering you on and holding my breath,
Don't want a part of beauty's grim death.
Sit tight, pretty pheasant, sit tight.

Soaring above the gun line, so high,
Straining with fear in your cackling flight:
Each take a turn and the guns aim and fire
A volley of shots. Will you die?
Your safety's assured by fate!
The peace of sweet summer awaits.
Sit tight, pretty pheasant, sit tight.

*Hilary Walker*

*Illustration: H Walker*

97